THE COUNTRY ESCAPE

JANE LOVERING

Boldwood

First published in Great Britain in 2020 by Boldwood Books Ltd.

This paperback edition first published in 2021.

1

A CIP catalogue record for this book is available from the British Library.

Paperback ISBN: 978-1-80048-563-1

Ebook ISBN: 978-1-80048-223-4

Kindle ISBN: 978-1-80048-224-1

Audio CD ISBN: 978-1-80048-230-2

Digital audio download ISBN: 978-1-80048-222-7

Large Print ISBN: 978-1-80048-225-8

Boldwood Books Ltd.

23 Bowerdean Street, London, SW6 3TN

www.boldwoodbooks.com

This book is dedicated to those who have suffered a stroke; to those who have kept a pony in a small orchard, those who live in tiny spaces, anyone who shares their home with more woodlice than they'd like and/or has the garden growing through into the house. And also to my offspring – Tom, Vienna, Fern, Will and Addie, for listening to my endless wittering on about imaginary people and places. Love you all.

1

'You've bought me a pony!'

As I sailed upwards from the warm comfort of sleep to the sharp-edged day, the words became part of my dream, and I was eleven, the air smelled of horse and the potential excitement that only an eleven-year-old can feel at the thought of mucking-out and cleaning tack into infinity. Then the excitement faded beneath an oncoming darkness, and I was awake, with my fourteen-year-old daughter bouncing on my feet.

'Wha'?' I said, less than elegant at this time on a September morning. Not that I'm all that elegant even in June, but there's something about the chill of a late summer morning that makes me think my mother's cardigan habit wasn't entirely for show. There was an extra duvet on the bed and I was wearing fleecy pyjamas.

'A pony!' Poppy bounced on my feet again, reduced by the prospect of a potential equine from the cynical, world-weary teenager to an overexcited nine-year-old. 'There's a pony in the orchard!'

As my dreams had also taken me back to our old life in

the London flat, with Luc, even the word 'orchard' wasn't computing. 'Wha'?' I said again, struggling upright under the bouncing. The cold air hit me as I exited the duvet and with it came the whole of past life, hitting me around the head. 'Oh.'

Whump went the sand-filled sock of memory as I stared at the bare walls of my bedroom, the tiny low window, which managed to let in as much cold air closed as open, and the dusty light of the old sun filtering through cobwebs I hadn't yet had the heart to disperse. Dorset, not London. Small house, not flat. And, apparently, an orchard, which I now remembered was what Poppy had decided to call the over-grown patch of land that adjoined the house. Too big and uncultivated to be a garden and too small to be a field, the borrowed dignity of a couple of mossy old apple trees had designated it its orchard status.

'Well?' Poppy had her hands on her hips. '*Did* you buy me a pony?'

With the habit of motherhood I noticed that she was still wearing her pyjamas, despite it being a school morning, and went straight to the practicalities. 'Go and get ready for school or you'll miss the bus.'

'Aren't you even going to *look*?' A humphy sigh, of the kind I'd got used to. 'Because if you didn't, and Dad didn't, then *someone* has parked a pony outside, and I'm pretty sure that's, like, a criminal offence?' She slithered the long body that she still despised, although it could only be a year or so away from being her best asset, off the bed and stomped across the creaky boards. 'And I'm going down to see him.'

'Get dressed first!' I called after her, pointlessly. It had been one of the many shocks of motherhood that the daughter who'd idolised me for the first five years of her life could come so quickly to the realisation that, basically, I was there to provide for her and keep her from harm, despite her increasing ability to outdo my ability to perform either of these tasks. She knew that I knew I couldn't *make* her do anything. There was a *lot* of reverse psychology going on, that's all I'll say.

In the spirit of 'don't do as I do', I dashed down the creaky, narrow-boarded stairs, trailing in the wake of Poppy, out across the stone-flagged kitchen into the orchard. The sun was up now, its low-level slant flinging the shadows of the trees back towards the house. There was a smell of incipient cider from a few windfalls, and the threatening hum of wasps starting the day's motor.

By the time I caught up, Poppy was at the far side of the field, where the narrow hawthorn hedge bordered the lane. And she was stroking the nose of something that could only be called a pony because the phrase 'badly put-together cow' was already taken. I called a token, 'Be careful,' across the grass but she didn't even acknowledge that I'd spoken.

'Isn't he beautiful?' she breathed. 'Where do you think he came from, Mum? Dad *wouldn't* give me a pony. Would he?' she finished on a note that was part acceptance of her father's fickle and profligate nature, and part a deep hope.

I looked over the slightly sway back of the piebald pony, to the gateway that led into the orchard. 'I'd say, just at a rough guess...' I tried to keep the sarcasm out of my words, but I knew she'd reinsert it anyway '... he's from that.'

Parked in the pull-in, where the lane became briefly wide enough between its tree-laden edges to allow a passing place, stood a caravan. One of the old-fashioned gypsy caravans, with a glorious bow top and painted front, a gilded split door surmounted by a little window and covered in gold-painted designs. The shafts were propped against the gate.

'Oh,' Poppy breathed, 'it's beautiful. He's beautiful. Do we get to keep him? If he's on our land, I mean?'

'No.' My voice was tight. I could smell the pony now, that mix of hay and newly mown grass and sweat and hooves and mud. 'Of course we can't. I'd better go and wake up the inhabitant and ask them to move.'

Poppy gave me a look. 'You better get dressed first, Mum. You don't want to look like a skank if you're knocking on someone's door at this time in the morning.'

In the spirit of not caving in to what my daughter thought of me, I climbed over the gate and cautiously approached the caravan door. I could feel the weight of Poppy's stare between my shoulder blades, and the horse wasn't helping either.

'Excuse me?' I tapped on the door. 'Hello?'

The door swung towards me, unlatched, on a waft of fried-food smells.

'Er, I live in the house...' I poked my head through. 'Your horse...'

The inside of the van was scrupulously tidy, beautifully ornate, and completely devoid of occupancy.

2

I have no idea how I managed to get Poppy to leave off cuddling the horse and go to school. She probably decided it was better to go and be able to boast about the pony that turned up in her field, than to stay at home with her mother being heavily disapproving at her. Either way, she dragged her uniform on and went to stand in the lane, where the minibus picked her up, together with a bunch of others from local farms, and dropped them all down in the village of Christmas Steepleton, from where they were all collected by the larger school bus. It was, as Poppy repeatedly told me, 'a drag', and if I'd been any kind of mother I wouldn't have removed her from her natural London habitat. Where her Starbucks addiction and her desire to try on every outfit in Oxford Street had been close to bankrupting me, but I hadn't mentioned that. I'd just told her that her dad and I finalising the divorce meant that the flat had to be sold, and the amount of money it gave me had just about been enough to buy Harvest Cottage and move to the Dorset coast.

Guilt, I told myself. Not just the thing making the outside

of that inexplicable deserted caravan shiny. I looked out of the kitchen window, where the sun was busy highlighting the fact that nobody had dusted or cleaned for what looked like a decade, across into the orchard. The pony was grazing as though he hadn't seen grass for weeks, although the width of him indicated he'd been extremely well fed up to this point. His black ears stuck up from the overlong grass that hid the rest of his face, looking like two skinny crows having a conversation, and the rest of his black-and-white-patched body seemed relaxed. I had a brief thought about laminitis, reasoned it was too late in the year for him to be affected, and went back to cleaning. He wasn't doing any harm, and it was possible that the caravan's occupant had just popped down to Steepleton to get some shopping. My lane was on the way, sort of, if you didn't mind squeezing between the overhanging oaks that lined it, before it climbed up and over the hill to join the main road and begin a final – and, in a horse-drawn caravan, probably fatal – drop down into the village. In the other direction lay another steep descent, a narrow ford and then miles of meandering grey tarmac, broken by weeds and salted with farm trackways, before it met the Bridport road.

Yes, that would be it. Someone had gone shopping and hadn't realised that Harvest Cottage was now occupied. After all, it had been empty for nearly five years, apparently, following a disputed bequest. Nobody had technically owned it, so nobody could sell it, and it had sat here in its damp fold in the Dorset hills with dereliction becoming an increasing likelihood. Once the whole 'who inherited the cottage' had been sorted out, it had hit the market just at the point that Luc and I had sold the flat. I'd been left with my half of the proceeds, enough to outright buy the little place. Luc had... actually, I wasn't entirely sure what Luc had done with his half. I didn't want to know. I didn't *need* to know. We were divorced. We only needed contact to talk about Poppy.

I suddenly realised that I'd been scrubbing so hard that I'd washed a layer of paint off the kitchen wall to reveal that a previous owner had thought that pale green was a suitable colour scheme for a room that already let in bilious levels of light. It would have been like cooking inside someone's hangover. I tipped the bucket of filthy water down the sink, which gurgled in a way that let me know that blockages were probably only a carelessly disposed-of teabag away, and saw the pony bring his head up sharply from the knee-level grass. He was staring around the corner, towards what was only my front door because it was at the opposite end of the cottage to the kitchen door.

There came a couple of raps on the woodwork. I was sure the windows rattled through the whole building.

'That had better be caravan person,' I muttered, wiping my hands down my front because I hadn't found the kitchen towel yet. 'And they can just pack that bloody animal up and go.'

I realised that the knocker had clearly thought the cottage was uninhabited when I threw open the door and the figure, shadowed by the overgrown blackcurrant bushes, jumped. 'Bloody hell, it's haunted!'

'No, it isn't. You knocked, I opened the door. Why would you knock if you didn't think anyone was here?'

'Politeness?' The voice was male, but the darkness of the combination of undergrowth, overhang and the fact I'd come from a brightly lit room to the shadowy front of the cottage, meant that he was just an outline. 'I've come about the caravan.'

'No need.' I was already turning away. 'Just hitch up your

horse and go, and I'd appreciate it if you'd remember that I live here now and didn't really like waking up to your horse eating my lawn.'

It wasn't, by any stretch of anyone's imagination, a lawn. But I thought it made me sound suitably disgruntled with cause.

'Er, okay.' The man shuffled from foot to foot. 'Only I think we've got a problem.'

I turned back and squinted at him. 'My only problem is that there's about fourteen hands of piebald eating my garden. Maybe you'd like to remove him? Before he gets as far as the rhubarb?'

There was an oppressively sweet smell from the branches that had been crushed by the man's passage up the garden path from the tiny front gate. It smelled a little like cat pee mixed with jam and I reminded myself to find out what kind of hellish horticulture was planted near the gate, and rip it out. Eventually.

'That's kind of the problem.' The man had a trace of a Dorset accent, still alien to my London-attuned ears. 'It's not my van. It belongs to Granny Mary, but she was taken ill last night, passing by this place. She stopped and put Patrick in your paddock before she called an ambulance, but she's up to Bridport hospital and they think she's had some kind of stroke. She called me and asked me to come and check up on Patrick. I wonder if you'd mind keeping an eye on things until she can get back to pick it all up?'

Oh, Lord. Maybe *this* was why my Streatham friends – none of whom had visited yet, despite the fact that they'd all said they'd come down for weekends – had warned me about life in the sticks. All this 'up in everyone's business'?

'Look, I'm not sure...'

'It's Patrick, really. I don't know how bad this stroke is – she's still communicating but I think it would take more than that to shut Mary up. I had her on the phone for an hour this morning to make sure I knew what to do. In fact, I think even death would have a tough job slowing Mary down. I reckon she'll be running round Steepleton as a corpse, trying to make sure everything goes her way.' There was a pause. 'Yeah, that's not a great image, now I come to think of it, sorry.'

A blackbird sang into the resulting silence.

'Well, I'm sorry, but the horse can't stay.' I wiped my hands down my front again. 'We've only been here two weeks, my daughter is protesting enough about having to change schools and I don't want her to have any excuse for not going, and, believe me, having to look after a horse that is going to have cleared all the grass from the orchard within a week will be excuse enough. Can't you arrange to have it all moved to wherever it is that you live?'

I tried to eyeball him strongly, but the fact that he stood in near-complete shadow and I was backlit by the sun streaming through from the kitchen whilst wearing an apron and rubber gloves like some kind of Vision of Nineteen Fifty, rather took the edge off.

'Granny Mary might have something to say about that.' The man shifted and some branches pinged around. It was a bit of a closely confined space at the front of the cottage, where the little gate onto the lane had clearly only ever been used as a last resort. The resulting mossy undergrowth had turned the whole of the path to the door, and most of the outside of the porch too, into something that Sleeping Beauty's prince would have approached with caution and a chainsaw. 'Look, I'm sorry. We seem to have got off on the wrong foot here. I haven't even introduced myself. Gabriel Hunter.'

A hand extended and I shook it without removing my rubber glove. 'Whichever foot we might be on,' I said, somewhat stiffly, also embarrassed that I hadn't taken the glove off, 'the horse has to go. The caravan can stay if we pull it into the field. It's probably not safe to leave on the side of the road like that, the lane is narrow enough as it is. But I can't look after a horse. The orchard is barely an acre – it's not enough grazing at this time of year, he's going to need hay and feed too, and then there's all the poo.'

'Good for the rhubarb,' said Gabriel, robustly. 'Granny Mary says you can use the van, if you want, to keep it aired out. Even couple up Patrick and take it round the lanes – it's a great way of seeing the countryside.'

I looked behind me through the house. The horse, who I now assumed went by the name of Patrick, was rubbing his backside against one of the trees to the accompaniment of over-ripe apples plopping down around him. One hit him square on the withers. He looked like an illustration in a pony book, drawn by someone with an eye for realism.

'I don't need to see the countryside. I live here,' I said, tartly. 'And I don't want to look after someone else's horse.'

The man sighed. 'Okay, yes. Sorry. I'm beginning to realise that Mary might not have thought this through.' A hand raised and was, presumably, running through his hair. 'Can I just come through and check him over? So I can tell her he's all right for now? I'll have to try to sort somewhere for him to go.'

I indicated, with a flopping yellow rubber hand, the path that squeezed its way around the outside of the cottage, between the wall and the overgrown hedge. Moss had furred its outline so it was hard to tell what was path and what was grass edging. 'You can go round that way.' He wasn't coming into my house, that was for certain. All those things I'd told Poppy about not letting people inside unless you knew them well were probably more related to London, but even so. 'I'll meet you out there.'

I closed the front door firmly, in case he was going to insist on the shortcut, and flew through the house whilst tearing off the rubber gloves. He was *probably* fine, but I hadn't even seen his face yet and that didn't inspire me with trust. Besides, I was starting to feel slightly proprietorial towards the horse, and if this bloke turned out to be a horse thief with no sense of discernment and a taste for beasts that looked like barrels on legs, well, I'd at least be there to help him load up.

When I reached the orchard, the man was already there. He was standing with his back to me, one hand on Patrick's neck and the horse's muzzle deep in his pocket. He was murmuring to him; the faint Dorset accent, the thick rays of sun striping down through the trees, and the hum of birds and bees made it feel like the closing-credit scene in some bucolic film. *Tess of the D'Urbervilles* swam briefly to mind, until I realised that that wasn't really the serene image I was looking for.

The blackbird sang again, now high in the apple tree.

Behind me, the kitchen door slammed in a gust, the badly fitted windows rattled, and the man and horse both looked up at me. Now in sunlight, I could see the man better. He was tall, long-haired, with one of those faces that look as though they've been designed by computer, all cheekbones and eyes and chin. He was wearing a pair of glasses so thick that his eyes were magnified, and a designer stubble that gave him the look of an off-duty Burberry model. With the piebald horse blowing softly at me over his shoulder, it was all a bit *Country Life* photo shoot for me.

'He's fine,' I said, stiffly, horribly aware of my hair tied up with a J-Cloth, and that my apron had a pattern of ducklings all across the pocket. 'He'll need some water though.'

The man, Gabriel, looked back at the horse, and murmured a few more soft words, then patted the rough neck and stepped away. 'Have you got a bucket? I'll leave him some and then if you could refill it?' He put his hands into the front pockets of his jeans, pulled them out again and then folded his arms, as though having to deal with limbs were a new problem for him. 'And then I'm going up to Bridport to slowly murder Granny Mary for putting us both in this position.'

He'd looked away again, watching the enormous splayed hooves picking their way past the tree roots, and his words had been quiet, but heartfelt. I immediately felt defensive on the part of the absent Granny Mary. 'Well, he's not doing any harm for now. At least she had the sense to put him somewhere with decent fencing, rather than leaving him roaming out on the lane.'

This elicited a small smile. 'Well, Patrick and the van are her pride and joy. Even something like a stroke isn't going to come between Mary and Patrick's welfare.'

Another silence resulted, broken only by the determined sound of equine teeth ripping up my grass. Eventually, because we were both just standing there, I cleared my throat. 'So, you're going to find somewhere else for him to go, and I'll just keep an eye on him in the meantime.' I spoke briskly, to break the deadlock. I had the feeling that if I didn't move this along a bit, he'd stand here in the orchard for the rest of the day, and I had paintwork to be washing down.

'Er. Yes.'

He still had his arms folded, and was staring at the ground.

'And I suppose we ought to pull the van in through the gate, to keep it off the road.' My apron flapped in the breeze, a little flag marking my status. 'Only I've got things to get on with, so...'

Now his head came up. 'Oh, yes, of course. I'm sorry. I was just thinking. I'm a bit... yes. Yes, of course.' He gave his head a quick shake, as though trying to lose something in the movement. 'Can you give me a hand?'

I opened the gate. A whirl of pockmarks showed where Patrick had come in in a hurry, pitting the entrance, and we had to struggle to pull the van through the ridged mud. But eventually, with each of us tugging one shaft, we dragged the surprisingly light vehicle in and parked it against the far hedge, with the shafts up on their rests. It looked very at home there, with its red bow roof squeezed between inquisitive bramble stems, the paintwork almost glowing as the sun caught it. The big yellow wheels with their red trim stood as stickily in the long grass as the pony did, and there was a certain similarity also in the squat wide body. Patrick, in the meantime, grazed near the kitchen door and took no notice of us gasping and pulling, until we stepped away from the van, when he ambled up to scratch his tail against the woodwork.

Gabriel gave me a grin that made him look less like a distracted computer programmer with a modelling contract. 'That should do. I can tell Granny Mary that it's all safe and cared for now. I've sent her a couple of pictures, so she'll know he's not tethered in the middle of the M5 being forced to eat his own knees.'

'But only temporarily. We agreed. You'll find somewhere else for him soon.'

'For Patrick. Can't the van stay?' He flipped hair away from his face with the back of his hand, and I noticed his glasses were askew. 'You could use it for...'

'Firewood?' I was being sarcastic, of course. There was no way anyone with a soul would chop this beautifully painted object up.

'A summerhouse? I mean, hopefully Granny Mary won't be in the hospital for long, just while they run the tests... and then she'll be back on the road.' The way his accent said 'road' made it sound like 'rowd' and my ears started to dwell on his voice. It had been his accent that had first attracted me to Luc, and I had to remind myself sternly how *that* had turned out: a desperate divorce and a daughter who was a cross between Emily Brontë and a character from *TOWIE*. A pleasant accent does not mean a nice person stands behind it.

A car engine slowed to a tick in the lane beyond the hedge. I heard the squeak sound of hawthorn branches being scraped past paintwork; the lane was really not a thorough-fare, although it seemed that the occasional non-critical satnav user got sent this way. We had heard the swearing, after they'd negotiated the tight lane only to find themselves faced with a slightly-too-deep-for-comfort ford at the bottom of the hill. At least they no longer had to contend with a wooden caravan in the only passing place for miles.

'Can I have your phone number?' He was still talking and I had to stop hearing the accent and start listening to the words.

'No.' I figured a flat refusal was best. What did he think I was, some floozy in a duck apron, who'd give her number to any man who asked? Even if he did look as though he should be on the cover of a magazine, minus those thick glasses and plus some proper clothes.

'Er. In case I need to get in touch about Patrick?' There

was no hint in his voice, or face, that he thought my saying no was anything other than normal. 'I've got a friend who might let me rent a field. I wouldn't want you to come home from, uh, whatever it is that you do and find him gone without a word.'

I opened my mouth to say that I didn't do anything, as yet, the market for French language teachers wasn't quite as open as I'd thought it might be, but I reasoned that he might think I was lying. I had my hair tied up with a dishcloth and an apron covered in cartoon ducklings. I didn't look like anything a responsible adult would trust with their children. 'Oh. Right,' was what I did say.

We exchanged phone numbers. I took my mobile out of the apron pocket to put his contact details in, and saw him suppress a smile. 'I'm washing down paintwork,' I said. 'We only moved in two weeks ago and it's a bit of a mess in there.'

'Hence the gloves?'

'No, it's my fetish,' I snapped, and instantly hated myself. 'I mean, yes. The stuff I'm using isn't good for the skin.'

'You're sugar soaping?' He adjusted his glasses, straightening them out and pushing them up his nose. 'No need to bother, to be honest. Modern paint will stick perfectly well if you just use water and some detergent.'

Patrick stomped back around and walked between us, which was good. It meant that my 'oh, great, another man waltzing in and telling me where I'm going wrong' face was hidden behind a fuzzy black and white body.

'I'll bear that in mind. Now, if you have to be off, I'll give Patrick some water when I've finished with the bucket. And yes, I will rinse it out properly. Goodbye.' I turned around sharply as some small birds fluttered out of the hedge, saw me moving and altered their flight pattern upwards.

'Ah, yes. Sorry.'

As the kitchen door had slammed shut, I'd have to go back in through the front door, so I headed down the side of the cottage, aware that Gabriel was following at my shoulder. Fortunately the gap was too narrow for Patrick to follow him, although the sound of a horse trying to get its bulk into an alleyway was one that would stay with me for a while.

We rounded the shoulder of the cottage, where the porch stuck out and narrowed the entryway even further. 'I'll hear from you soon, then,' I said, turning to go into the darkness of the porch, and jumping backwards to smack Gabriel in the face with the back of my head when I realised someone was already in there, and there was a car parked outside the gate.

'Hello, Katie,' said a voice from the darkest recesses of hell and also my porch.

My ex-husband had come to visit.

3

We sat in the kitchen, with Gabriel holding a tea towel to his bleeding nose and occasionally dabbing at the incipient black eye where his glasses had impacted. I'd just about stopped apologising to him and offering him ice, but it was touch and go.

Luc had pulled out a chair at the little table and was sitting with his legs outstretched. Comfortable. Settled in.

'So, Katie,' he said, his French accent sounding exotic in the confines of the little stone-flagged room. 'You moved all this way, huh? To *this*...' and he threw his arms wide, indicating presumably the poverty of my kitchen. 'I never thought you could live this way in such a...' he groped for an epithet '... a backwater.'

Gabriel had flinched at the outflung arms, which had resulted in more blood. I handed him another tea towel. This was horrible. No, this was beyond ordinary horrible and into *Game of Thrones* horribility. All we needed now was a dragon; we'd already got the blood and the psychopath.

'You lost the ability to comment on my life when we divorced.' I threw Gabriel an apologetic look. I really didn't want dirty laundry to be spread out in front of this perfect stranger, but I didn't feel I could ask him to leave when he was seeping bodily fluids into my Laura Ashley finest linen weave. 'How *is* Mariette, by the way?'

It was a low blow, but the quickest way I could think of to sum up the break-up of our relationship. Yes, I was the cliché, the wife left for a younger, prettier and more successful woman. Although, in my case, I didn't bear Mariette any grudges, more a kind of sideways sympathy along with the knowledge that she wasn't the first, and would, undoubtedly, not be the last of Luc's 'conquests'.

'She is very good, thank you.' Luc was dressing twenty years younger now, I noted. Slim chinos and a collarless grey shirt, his hair smooth and still dark, damn him. I found new grey hairs every day, but then I had to deal with Poppy. 'I came to see our daughter.'

'She's at school. Obviously.'

Gabriel looked as if he was trying to fade into the background, despite the blood. He kept looking behind him towards the kitchen door, as though he wanted to make a break for it. I didn't blame him. This was awkward, with a capital A.

'Term has started already?' Luc did the Gallic shrug, which didn't surprise me. We'd been together for nearly fourteen years, and for most of those, plus the year after we'd separated, he'd had a daughter whose comings and goings had regularly bemused him. Luc had been so busy doing Luc that he'd never had the brain-space to contemplate the fact that Poppy might need new clothes, a regular schedule or, in fact, food.

'Last week. We spent a week moving in and then she started at the local school.'

'And what year is she, now?'

'Year Ten. Look, I don't mean to be rude, but...'

Luc looked at his watch. 'Ah. Maybe, then, I will come back later.'

'I'd prefer it if you rang before you came, next time.' I threw another glance at Gabriel, who looked as though he was desperately trying not to listen in, and Luc misread the look.

'Of course! You will be wanting to start your new life.' Another arm-fling, taking in Gabriel this time, who now had taken his glasses off to pat gently at his swollen eye.

'Yes,' I said gently. 'I do. You're welcome to see Poppy any time, of course you are, she'll be over the moon, but—' How did I sum it up? That I couldn't have this glamorous Frenchman wafting in and out of my life any more, trailing his string of disappointed girlfriends and his trust fund. I was glad he'd met Mariette and decided to settle down. It might mean I knew where he was for more than a fortnight. 'We aren't together any more, Luc. It's just Poppy.'

Luc stood up and Gabriel flinched again. 'Well, I go. I will call Poppy, maybe I will see her tonight.'

'I'll tell her you came by.' I stood up too, trying to shuffle him towards the front door.

Luc paused, looking out of the kitchen window. 'There is a horse out there,' he observed.

'Patrick,' Gabriel and I said together, him slightly muffled by two layers of tea towel.

Luc raised his eyebrows. 'I thought you said our daughter would be a horse person over your dead body?'

He said it as though it was a personal accusation. As

though I'd spent all those years denying our daughter an experience from sheer bloody-mindedness, rather than the fact that London wasn't exactly known for its acres of free riding space. Yes, there were riding schools, but...

'He's mine,' Gabriel said nasally. 'Just staying for a few days.'

Another Gallic shrug, as though Luc had forgotten all those arguments over what Poppy should be allowed to do. As though nothing I had said had ever been important or taken notice of. But then, here was a man who'd promised to love me forever. Who'd met and married me during my year in France where everything had seemed charmed and easy, whose money had greased wheels I hadn't even known existed and whose charisma should have come with a health warning.

Gabriel and I sat in silence, listening to the rumble of Luc's car engine as he slowly edged it around in the lane and headed back up the track towards civilisation and chilled Chardonnay. We stared at different parts of the room; my gaze was riveted on the crack in the deep enamel sink, he seemed to be finding the dresser on the opposite wall absolutely fascinating. The sun had moved out of the room now and the smell of damp was back. A few woodlice scurried busily across the stone floor, and I concentrated on those for a while.

'Sorry about that,' I said eventually. 'My ex-husband and his lack of boundaries.'

'It's fine,' came the muted reply.

'How's the nose?'

'Um.' The tea towel lifted. 'It's nearly stopped bleeding.'

'I'm really sorry.' The woodlice had shuffled off under the door to the walk-in pantry. I made a mental note to never keep anything that wasn't in tins in there.

'It was an accident.' A cautious finger poked at the bridge of his nose. 'It was, wasn't it? I mean, you didn't do it just to keep me captive here?'

'Stephen King?' I looked at him directly now.

'Maybe. I read too much. Well, audio books, mostly. I've got a Kindle but it's on about two words to a page.' A bit of a grin appeared under the layers of cotton. His glasses were on the table and I could see again how thick the lenses were. 'Eyesight's not great.'

Without the glasses, and even with his nose swollen and his eye discoloured by the spreading bruise that the back of my head had caused, he looked model-like. Cheekbones like cheese wire and almond-shaped eyes that, in this now-shadowed room, looked almost black. Dark stubble outlined his jaw and highlighted his mouth. It seemed an awful shame to waste such good looks on me, who currently had as much desire to appreciate handsomeness as I did to take up deep-sea fishing. Which was none.

Luc was handsome. He'd also got an attractive accent. He was the kind of mistake I would only make once in a lifetime. Besides, for all I knew Gabriel was married, gay, asexual, violently insane and a narcissistic fantasist. I hoped, for his sake, that he wasn't all of those simultaneously.

'Well,' I began. I didn't know how to go about getting him out of my kitchen gracefully, particularly when I'd just broken his nose, given him a black eye and subjected him to Luc. 'I ought to get on with, you know, stuff.' I glanced at the bucket of now cold and scummy water in the corner where I'd been washing walls. I actually wanted a glass of wine and maybe a bacon sandwich, but felt that offering those to Gabriel would be tantamount to saying, 'I'm a divorced woman in her mid-thirties who wants to work on a drink problem and gaining four stone in solitude and misery.' So, I didn't say anything.

'What colour were you thinking of painting it?' He was looking at the bucket too.

'Not sure yet.' Then, with some suspicion, because he was looking around the room again. 'Why?' I really hoped he wasn't going to make me an offer to buy the cottage. Maybe he was one of those 'house flippers' from the programmes that Poppy liked to watch and then gossip about with her friends; where people bought derelict places really cheaply, did them up in a cursory fashion and then sold them on before the rampaging damp and lack of underpinnings became evident. And then I felt a bit insulted, because Harvest Cottage was nowhere near derelict. And had very good underpinnings. The damp was a question yet to be resolved.

'Have you thought about using it as a location?' The question was slow, although that might have been the amount of tea towel it was filtered through.

'Yes. It's a location for us to live in. I thought the boxes of stuff all over the place would be a giveaway.'

A quick headshake. 'I mean for films.' A pause while he looked at the blood again. 'I work for the company filming down in Steepleton at the moment. They're making a detective series, called *Spindrift*, just got the green light to go to a second series, and we're looking for locations.' Another quick look around the kitchen. 'And this would be great. If you don't do too much to it.'

A woodlouse outlier hurtled across the flags from the back door to the pantry and flung itself through the crack. The room was so quiet I could almost hear its legs scrabbling.

'Do they... pay?' I asked, slowly. Trying not to sound desperate.

'Oh, yes. Depends on how long we need to shoot for, but, yep, they pay pretty well.' He took his glasses off the table and slid them back on. 'It's got a good look. Unkempt.' There was a patch over near the window where grass had grown in under the wall. 'But picturesque,' he added quickly. 'And we need a location where we can film an entire storyline without being mugged by tourists. This is pretty isolated.'

Well. Money would be good. Luc was paying for Poppy, and the money from the flat had bought the cottage outright, but there would be bills I hadn't foreseen yet. The cottage didn't have central heating and, in *Game of Thrones* parlance, winter was coming. I didn't have great hopes of the little wood-burning stove to heat the whole place, and the electricity tripped out if you plugged in more than four devices at once.

And I didn't have a job.

'I'll leave you to think about it.' Gabriel stood up. Indoors he looked taller; his head nearly rapped the beams. 'You've got my number.'

'I've also got the horse.'

'Very true.'

'Did you drive up here?' I began to wonder. I hadn't heard a vehicle before Luc's, not since the early morning milker had dashed through on his motorbike on his way to the next valley.

Another headshake. 'Walked. I don't drive. Eyesight, you see. Not only can I not read a number plate at the required distance, I can't even see the car the number plate is attached to.'

'That must be...' I tailed off. I had no idea what it must be like. Annoying? Or life changing?

'It's fine. You're only two miles from Steepleton, if you go up over the cliff, and walking is a far better way to find locations than driving past. But, can I just ask for a quick tour? So that I can take a package plan back to HQ? Often we only use one room, but with this place – I think we could use the whole cottage.'

'You want a tour. Of the cottage.' I was desperately trying to remember if I'd picked yesterday's pants up from the floor and whether my bedside reading looked suitably erudite. Had Poppy left shampoo and wet towels all over the bathroom? Was her room even possible to enter?

'Just really quickly.' Another grin. 'I only want to get a general idea. I won't judge, I'm not your mother.'

No, sunshine, you certainly aren't, I thought, leading him slightly grudgingly out of the kitchen. He looked around the tiny hall, peered into the bare-floored living room, where our huge angular couch took up space like a dowager duchess in a squat. Up the stairs to the creaky landing, and a quick glance into my bedroom – where pants were not in evidence – and Poppy's, which was ninety per cent K-pop posters. He ignored the bathroom, which was just as well.

'It's a lovely little place.' I finally got him out of the front door. 'If you give me the okay, I'll put it forward. We would need to spend some time shooting here – we've got a storyline coming up about a serial killer, set to run through all nine episodes. I think this would make a great location for our killer to live.'

'Well, I certainly won't lie awake tonight worrying about *that* now,' I said, slightly tartly.

He smiled, uncertainly. 'Call it recompense for the broken nose. Oh, and don't do too much work to the inside. We would need that slightly neglected vibe.'

'*Slightly neglected vibe*,' I muttered to myself, once I'd closed the door on him. Harvest Cottage wasn't neglected. It was... it was... full of potential.

Even the woodlice laughed at that.

4

'Hate it.' Poppy swirled inside, dropping her school bag on the floor just inside the door. 'Hate it, hate it, hate it. Why couldn't we have gone to live with Grandma Bryant?'

The question took me aback a little. I followed her through, down the hallway and into the kitchen, which I'd tried to make smell homely and welcoming by baking some rock buns. 'Because Grandma Bryant lives in a flat?' And besides, my mother and I had a relationship that was uneasy at the best of times. Destructive at worst.

Poppy trailed through, coat half off one shoulder. 'Yeah, but we could have stayed there until we found somewhere near my school. My *proper* school, not this dump that they call a school round here, where there's only four forms in Year Ten and most of the sixth form are dorks. Who the hell am I meant to have a crush on when there's no lush sixth formers?' She flung open the back door and went out into the orchard, where Patrick, now complete with water bucket, was standing dreaming under one of the apple trees, tail slowly swishing. 'I could have riding lessons now.'

'No,' I said quickly. 'Money is going to be tight, and this isn't a riding pony. I doubt he's even broken to ride. Besides, he's not going to be here much longer.' I started telling her about Gabriel and Granny Mary, and Patrick, but she clearly wasn't listening.

'You've moved the van.'

'Yes, Gabriel and I pulled it in here to keep the road clear. No, don't go inside...'

'I'm not going to *touch* anything.' I followed her up the steps and we stood in the tiny doorway, peering in. 'Look, it's got everything!'

At the far end of the van was a built-in bed, half hidden behind curtains. Fitted cupboards lined the walls, a tiny stove jutted its chimney up through the roof and a sink and hotplate took up the rest of the space. There were photographs and ornaments on all the flat surfaces. I frowned, and poked a small china figurine of a dancing girl experimentally.

'You're not supposed to touch,' Poppy said, gleefully.

'Just wondering how it doesn't all fall over every time the van moves.'

'And?' Clearly holding herself back from dashing around the van opening the cupboards and exclaiming, she stared out of the small window, as though our orchard were transformed into fairyland from being seen from inside this magical space. With all the drapings and decorations, the bunches of dried herbs and flowers that hung from the roof, the ornate soft furnishings and velvet curtains, the inside of the van had the feel of a faery bower. It seemed as if Titania had just popped out for a moment to gather some dew.

'Blu-Tack.'

'It's gorgeous.'

'And it smells of sausages. Maybe we should leave the window open for a bit to air it out.' I pushed the glazed top half of the door and it swung, separate from the bottom half. 'Come on, out. You wouldn't want someone poking around in your bedroom, would you?'

We backed slowly down the steps. Almost childlike in her wonder, Poppy traced the outline of one of the intricate designs painted on the door. 'It's beautiful.' Then, with a glance at me, 'I mean, completely shit to live in, obviously. But, maybe, you could, like, live out here and I could have the cottage.'

'Nope.'

'It would be great though! I could have my friends down to stay from school and it would be fantastic and cool and you'd be out here to... to keep an eye on us and cook and everything. But far away, obvs.' She waved a hand. 'It's just all really old-fashioned. Perfect for you, Mum.'

At the sight of all the activity around the van door, Patrick's head came up and he whinnied a short, high sound. His neck arched like a destrier and he trotted across the orchard towards us, mane and tail flowing out behind him and his big, feathered legs swishing the grass. When there was no sign of his owner coming out of the van, he slowed to a walk and nudged the shafts with his pink nose.

'Poor lad. He misses her.' I gave the firm shoulder an absent-minded pat. The smell of warm horse, newly munched grass and the faint overlay of leather was horribly familiar in a way that made me feel a bit sick. 'I hope Gabriel can find somewhere for him to go soon.'

'Can I have my tea out here?' Poppy sat on the steps. 'It's nice. I've had geeky little year eights trying to talk to me all day. I guess they don't see many people round here that they aren't all related to. They all want to know what London is like, poor bastards.'

'Poppy...'

'Sorry. But they are. Oh, and Dad rang, he's down this way, said he'd pick me up from school tomorrow and take me out for dinner.'

'That's very nice of him.'

She looked in my face, searching for a trace of sarcasm maybe, but losing interest with the typical attention span of the fourteen-year-old. 'You haven't done much painting.'

'Well, no.' Again, I began telling her about Gabriel and the possibility of the cottage being used as a location. I didn't know why; she hadn't listened the first time. But when I mentioned the word *Spindrift*, she turned away from her patting of Patrick, with a dramatic slowness that I was clearly meant to notice and remark upon.

'Did you say they might want to film *Spindrift* here? *Here?*' She pointed to the cottage, as though I might have thought she meant the county of Dorset in a less specific way. '*Really?*'

'Well, I haven't said yes yet, but it would be a way to get some money in before we need to start lighting fires and—' I stopped talking because Poppy was currently giving me a stare that indicated that her entire face might fall off any moment now.

'Oh. My. God,' she enunciated. 'Do you know what this *means*? No, cos you're really old and you only watch programmes that have, like, antiques and stuff in. Oh. My. God. I have to go and tell Shawnia and Emily-Rose.' She fumbled in the pocket of her half-worn coat for her phone. 'This is *big stuff*, Mum. This means Davin might come here!'

'Who the hell is Davin?' I asked her retreating back, but was answered with nothing but the excited squeals of her reconnection with whichever of her London friends had answered first. Patrick looked at me. He had unsymmetrical black markings, so one eye had a rakish pirate patch while the rest of his face was almost completely white. This white head sat on a black neck, which devolved into a body with random large black continents spread over a grass-stained white sea. His mane and forelock were long and contained varied examples of local flora and his feet were the size of the blue plaques you get outside houses where interesting people have lived.

'Please tell me you aren't broken to ride,' I whispered to him.

He cocked a lazy black ear, and tipped a hind leg to rest on its hoof edge. He looked as though explosions could happen and he'd still stand here, resting, with his lower lip all droopy and a bee tangled in his forelock. Broken to ride or not, it could only be a matter of time before Poppy decided to try sitting on him. I hoped Gabriel could find him a new residence before then.

The sun was dropping fast now. September twilight was thicker here where there were no street lights, no nearby conurbations to illuminate the sky. Trees slid into outline; inside the cottage Poppy turned on her bedroom light and a beam of yellow spilled out across the side of the house as I left Patrick to his dreaming and went back in.

One of the reasons – one of the *many* reasons, I suspected, most of which I hadn't found yet – that Harvest Cottage hadn't been snapped up as a holiday home was the awkward crookedness of the layout. It looked as though it had once been a cob and thatch pig house, but added to and extended over the years in a variety of materials, so that it now resembled something that the Weasleys from *Harry Potter* might have lived in. The north-facing porch, which meant any visitor was incognito in the mossy, damp front entryway, the hallway so narrow that we'd had to post the sofa into the front room through the window, in pieces. The staircase, which, contrary to all convention, didn't go up against one wall, but was freestanding up the middle of the cottage. Two bedrooms and a bathroom that seemed to have been an original hayloft, all randomly arranged, and beamed in such a way that any quick movements meant a banged forehead and a lot of swearing. I'd already learned to crouch and scuttle around the place, like an obsequious servant. It was bizarre.

But, I reminded myself as I threw some wood into the range cooker to heat up for dinner, it was *mine*. Luc might not approve of its smallness, but then the man had been brought up in apartments in a chateau, he'd find Buckingham Palace a bit crowded. He probably thought I was mad, moving to Dorset, but here it was affordable and there was countryside. I hadn't realised how much I'd missed countryside until I saw Harvest Cottage. I'd thought I wanted city streets, blue emergency lights and sirens filling up the night; people coming and going at all hours and a Waitrose around the corner. Poppy's school only a short Tube ride away, all the attractions and occupations of museums and galleries and exhibitions at the weekends.

Whilst here... here was the wind in the trees. Birdsong, grass, and, if you listened very carefully on still nights, the gentle exhalation of the sea moving against the distant cliffs. There was a small bay within walking distance, out of the cottage and across several fields of short-grazed grass and barley stubble, down a steep cliff path. A tiny patch of shingly sand and rock pools, which sloped suddenly to take your feet and leave you bobbing in the icy water, shrieking and gasping.

Poppy, of course, loved it. And hadn't been down there since we moved in.

The range bubbled and I put a pan of stew across its hotplate. The range heated the water for the cottage but made no noticeable dent in the chill that crept across the stone floor as soon as the sun went down, because of the air coming in through the leaky windows. I winced at the draught and made a note that we'd need thick curtains at the very least, before winter. The windows needed replacing, as did both chimneys and one wall, but we'd get through this year first. Once I'd got a job, we could think about renovating the place rather than just redecorating and firefighting the woodlice, who seemed to regard Harvest Cottage as their own personal property and thoroughfare.

The blackbird, in the hedge now, sang the night in. I wondered whether blackbirds ate woodlice.

5

A couple of weeks went past. I held off doing any painting, but did manage to unpack some of the boxes that had travelled with us from London, the contents of which looked horribly urban in this tiny, thick-walled space.

I tried to arrange the asymmetrically striped black and white cushions on the sofa, so that they looked comfortable, rather than like the 'room accents' they were bought to be. If this room *had* an accent, I mused, it would be rural Dorset, not the sharp and edgy that we'd gone for in the two floors of the five-storied old Georgian town house that had provided our accommodation in London. There, bare floors and exposed woodwork was a statement that said, 'I can afford to cover all this area in lavish carpeting and internal walling, but I am carefully choosing not to.' In the cottage, bare floors were necessary until we got the damp under control and exposed woodwork was what was left where the paint had flaked off. It was very different. Two of the brambles from the orchard had climbed in through the pantry window and, despite my regularly cutting them off with the scissors, kept infiltrating the shelving, and every time I opened the door it was like *The Day of the Triffids*. I couldn't wait for autumn to really get under way and stop the relentless growth.

Patrick was still in the orchard. Apart from one brief text from Gabriel Hunter checking up on him and telling me that the cottage was 'a possible' for location work, I'd not heard from him. Poppy continued to hate her new school, doing homework intermittently and, according to the notes in her planner, not really applying herself to any of the subjects she'd chosen to study.

'I chose *last year*!' My accusations that she wasn't working hard enough were not warmly received. 'Pasty Greggs was really cool! Now I've got Miss Thompson for music and she makes us listen to *Beethoven*! That's, like, against my human rights and stuff.'

Poppy had no idea what she wanted to do when she left school. Apart from being a YouTube star, or a vlogger/influencer, there weren't many careers that interested her, and her monied father's attitude to life being 'you can just float around doing what interests you, making little bits here and there and being largely supported by your family' really wasn't going to take her very far, unless she was going to specialise in following bands across the country and take A levels in 'interesting hair colours'.

'Got an A in French though,' she pointed out, thrusting a pile of notes under my nose. 'So, there's that.'

'You've been bilingual since you could talk – it's hardly an achievement!'

Poppy sighed. 'Don't take it out on me that you're stuck here all day. *I* didn't ask to move to the Depths of Despair, did I? We could have still been in London, you'd have your teaching and I'd be getting all As and still going out with Damien!'

The door refused to slam. It was slightly too big for the frame and had to be dragged across the floor in order to close, but the slam was implicit. 'And it's *not* hormones!' was her passing shot as she stomped upstairs to a more satisfactorily slam of her bedroom door. 'You've ruined my life!'

I stood under the bare bulb in the living room and took several deep breaths. I'd already had a lengthy phone conversation with a couple of old friends back in town, who had only managed a small amount of sympathy with me; their jobs were over-pressured and fraught and they clearly imagined life in the countryside to be very different from the reality. I really couldn't ring them back to complain about my teenage daughter. My best friend, Lottie, was struggling with nursery school placements for her small son and juggling her teaching job on top, Arlene was dealing with a sick mother and resentful husband and Basia was on stress leave and contemplating a return to Poland. Here I stood amid the silence of my bought-and-paid-for cottage – a wailing daughter didn't really score that highly in the tension stakes.

But I wanted to talk to *somebody*. Apart from some exchanges about the weather in the supermarket in Bridport, and the encounter with Gabriel, I'd barely spoken to a soul since we moved in. Patrick was not a great conversationalist, and had nudged me hard enough to spill my tea when I'd sat on the van steps and tried to interest him in the trials and tribulations of life. So, when my phone rang, I grabbed it with an out-of-proportion gratitude.

'Ah, there you are.'

The gratitude dissipated quickly in the face of my mother's disapproving tone.

'Hello, Ma.' A long pause. 'How are you?'

'I am well.' Another pause. 'And you? Are you safely moved to... Dorset?' The slight gap told me that she'd had to look up my new location, probably in her little red book. 'I'm just telephoning to tell you that I'm off to Sydney next week, probably won't be back until Christmas. You know, in case you needed me.'

I perched on the arm of the sofa, the velvety fabric catching at my jeans like tiny fists. 'Well, thank you for letting me know. Have a good time with Aunt Christie, won't you?'

These conversations with my mother were so underrun with currents of tension that they practically stood up on their own. Our relationship was cool, practical, distant; she sent presents for Poppy and saw her once or twice a year, always let me know of her own whereabouts. In return, I sent flowers for her birthday and Mothers' Day, a personalised gift for Christmas, and the approved condolence cards when one of her circle died. All our interactions were very much based in the present; we had erased our past and it was never spoken of.

'I will. Goodbye, Katherine.'

And that was it.

Other women, I knew, could have told their mothers about the isolation, the loneliness, the fear of failure. The cold dampness at night, when I lay awake listening to the distant sea or the rain against the windows, worrying about never working again at the grand old age of thirty-four. About my ultimately unsuccessful marriage, the lack of local jobs, the crumbliness of the cottage and the fourteen-plus hands of piebald squatter in the orchard. But not me. And the gap between the relationship I wanted with my mother and the one I had, and the currently strained relationship I had with my daughter, made me sit for longer than I should have done under that bare, swinging bulb.

I was eventually brought out of my dark thoughts by the fact that my phone was buzzing an incoming text against the palm of my hand. Maybe my mother had thought of something to add? I was about to lay it down without looking, when I saw the name on the screen.

G Hunter:
Sorry I've not been in touch. We've had a meeting and I'd like another chat about using your place as a location. Any chance we could meet up? There's a really nice pub just outside Steepleton if you're free this evening...

I didn't even think twice. I texted back.

What time and what's the name of the pub?
PS Patrick is fine, but needs to move.

G Hunter:
It's The Grapes, up on the Bridport road. Eight o clock?
We can talk about Patrick too.

I'd been hoping for plans to move the pony, even the promise of an immediate single-horse trailer on the road. As it was, Patrick was running out of grazing in the orchard, and some recent rain had caused him to form a mud trail from the back of the field to the kitchen door, where he often stood disconcertingly staring in at me through the rattling glazing.

'I'm going out for a while later,' I called up the stairs, although Poppy probably had her earphones in and music blasting from her phone.

There was a moment of quiet and then her door opened a crack. 'What?'

I repeated myself. It wasn't an unusual experience. 'I'm going to meet up with the man who might use the cottage for a location.' Why I had to justify myself, I wasn't sure.

'Oh. *Oh!* Is this the bloke that knows Davin? Only, this boy on my bus, Rory, he's in Year Twelve, he's a bit of an idiot with a stupid haircut but he talks to me so there's that, well, *he* says his mum runs this café, right, and he knows Davin, and his mum's boyfriend, who I *think* is called Neil but that might be this other guy, he does sound on the new series! Probably a load of bollocks and he's just trying to impress me.'

Well, at least she was still talking to me. I wasn't sure if the stream of consciousness was better than the grunty silences; it took more processing but if you could winnow the sense out of it, there was often a giveaway or two to be gleaned. In this case, the name Rory. It sounded as though Poppy might have made a friend.

'Yes, we're going to have a chat about the cottage. And Patrick.'

'You can't send Patrick away, Mum. You *can't*.' The door closed again. It didn't slam, but that was probably only due to the amount of stuff on the floor preventing it. The bulb swung as Poppy walked across the floor above, throwing weird shadows across the room.

I still hadn't quite got used to the darkness out here; the way it came creeping in so early, like a lodger returning before the landlady had got the hoovering done and hoping not to be noticed. September had settled firmly over Dorset with cool nights giving way to warm days and the leaves beginning to brittle and brown on the trees. There was a smell in the air of ripe blackberries and burning and I had an almost atavistic urge to make jam, even though I'd never made jam in my life and hadn't even read the ingredients on the side of the jars that we always bought in Waitrose.

It was nearly seven o'clock. If I was going to meet Gabriel, then I had to get a move on. I was still wearing the clothes I'd, quite frankly, been wearing for two weeks. Washing down walls was as far as I'd got with the whole 'redecorating' thing, but it wasn't an activity that lent itself to designer clothing, so it was still jeans and an oversized shirt. The rubber gloves came and went, particularly when I was cleaning floors and picking up Patrick's poo from the orchard. The bucket had gone on timeshare.

Showering was probably optimistic. The electric shower spat alternate gobbets of hot and cold water, so the temperature was more of an average than an actual, and it had a tendency to throw the trip switch out. I settled for washing my face, combing my hair and putting on a pair of clean jeans and a T-shirt and jacket. 'The Grapes' could be anything from a spit and sawdust pub frequented only by locals to a gourmet bistro with a universe of Michelin stars and a clientele recruited from the TV actors that lived nearby. I reasoned that this outfit would fit in with either eventuality, and, with instructions to Poppy to finish her homework and ring me if she needed anything, I headed off.

My tiny Kia was perfect for driving the local lanes. I'd resisted Luc's urging to buy a 4 x 4 wagon for 'safety', and it was just as well because the narrow road to the top of the cliff, with its overhanging bracken and hawthorn, would have challenged anything much wider. I'd not really taken much notice when I'd first visited, still too shell-shocked by Luc's declaration that he was selling the flat, although I had taken note of the removal company's select and ripe language when they tried to get a full-sized lorry down as far as the cottage. Once out onto the lane that ran along the cliff, things got wider and easier and I wound my window down a little way to enjoy the chilly air, which brought in the smell of the sea. Up here, away from the constricting trees, there was a feeling of openness, the fields were grassy stretches of sheep behind gates, and the sky was huge overhead. Tucked into our little hillside, we didn't get a lot of sky, so I wound the window down further and stared up at the pinpricked blackness as it unspooled above me.

I met a crossroads and turned towards Bridport, ignoring the signs to Christmas Steepleton. I'd only been down to the little seaside village once or twice and it had been full of lorries and cars then. Presumably filming for *Spindrift* was under way, or at least in the heavily planning stage, and the lack of parking and actual shops that didn't sell tourist seaside stuff had kept me from returning. About a mile along the road, which was otherwise devoid of any buildings, was a blaze of lights and a full car park. I turned in, squeezed the Kia into a tiny corner space – another good reason not to have a big 4 x 4 – and somewhat hesitantly made my way around the building to the door.

A group of people were smoking outside, all laughing and jostling over a single lighter. I had one of those moments, when you *know* you are a twenty-first-century woman in possession of all her rights to enter a pub, yet internally there's still a whisper from eighteen-ninety womanhood, when going into a pub solo was the mark of a woman touting for custom. I had to seize my courage and ball it up in both hands, take a deep breath and open the door.

Nobody noticed me. I'd been a little bit worried that there might be a Slaughtered Lamb moment of quiet and everyone turning to the door, but the crowded warmth and chatter inside didn't miss a beat. I shouldered my way in and looked around.

'Hi there!' Gabriel was waving to me from a corner table just inside the door. 'Sit down. This is Tansy Merriweather, who's been in charge of location finding until now, and Keenan, our director. They've got a few questions for you. What are you drinking?'

Maybe it was something about Dorset – something in the air? – that made this easy kind of familiarity breed without contempt. I found myself chatting easily away to both Tansy and Keenan, learning about *Spindrift* and their places in the team.

'I'm going more over to managing the café over at Warram Bay,' Tansy said. She was small and pretty and had the slightly scrunched-up face of someone who spends a lot of time trying to think about what they say before they say it. 'Working too closely with Davin was making us bring too much work home. When I realised we spent a whole weekend just talking about filming, I decided it was time to get out, hence—' She waved a hand to indicate Gabriel, who was still standing at the bar.

'My daughter keeps mentioning Davin,' I said. 'You're a couple?'

'Yes. It's a bit like befriending a wild animal,' Tansy said. 'But he's okay really. If your daughter wants to spend some time on set...'

'She will, if we film at the cottage.' Keenan, who was short, plump, balding and almost the exact antithesis of what I'd previously thought TV directors would look like, said, over his gin.

'Oh, yes, I suppose she will. But I'm handing this one over

to Gabriel. I need to take more of a back seat this year, and managing the café is a bit less pressurised and has less of Davin shouting in it.'

'Tansy's part-owner of the café,' Keenan mock-whispered, hooking a slice of lime over his glass rim. 'And Gabriel is cheap and local. He's told us a bit about your place. It sounds... well, it sounds horrible, but I expect you like it. Got any pictures?'

I pulled out my phone and showed them the estate agent's pictures that had made me fall in love with Harvest Cottage in the first place. We discussed access and, when Gabriel finally fought his way through the crush at the bar and brought my drink over, we talked about layout and, finally, money.

Keenan named a figure that would help get us through the winter. Logs were expensive and we still needed carpet and curtains and fewer woodlice. After Christmas I would start looking for local teaching jobs again or apply to be in the bank of teachers to cover absences, but in the meantime payment for use of the cottage would get us through. It would be a squeak, but I was damned if I'd ask Luc for additional money.

We arranged a day for Keenan to come with some of the team to make sure that technicalities I didn't really grasp would work, and then he and Tansy went off back to Steepleton, leaving me with Gabriel.

'So, when is Patrick going?' I felt a bit awkward. I mean, obviously this wasn't a date, more of a business meeting, but it had been a long time since I'd been alone in a pub with a man. In fact, had I ever? I'd met Luc when I was nineteen, there had only been brief passing boyfriends before that, and Luc would have died rather than hang around in village pubs drinking cider and playing darts like this crowd.

Gabriel pushed his glasses up his nose. 'Um. Yes. Bit of a tricky one there,' he said, staring down into his pint glass of yellow bubbles. 'I don't know if Kee mentioned it...'

Actually Keenan had talked about a lot of stuff, but I'd mostly been focused on the money, so he could have mentioned anything and I might not have noticed.

'... and it was originally a pig,' Gabriel was continuing. 'But I was talking about Patrick being in the orchard and he thinks a horse might work better. I mean, obviously he won't be coming in the house, but, well. They might work Granny Mary's van in too. So, if he could stay, just until filming finishes?'

I thought of the stomped-mud path. Of the retreating grass and the patch on the largest apple tree where Patrick rubbed his tail. Of the big face that would appear at the window and gaze balefully at me from time to time. Of the fact that Poppy kept on about riding lessons.

'I don't know.' I put my glass down firmly. 'There's not really enough grass now. He's going to need hay and – does your granny give him hard feed? It must take some energy to pull that van and he's not getting that from just grass, not in winter. Does he need a rug? And a farrier will have to take his shoes off if he's not going to be working for a while.'

Gabriel blinked at me over his drink. His glasses magnified his eyes so much that it looked like a special effect. 'She's not actually my granny,' he said, and it sounded as though he'd picked on the least actionable of my statements. 'It's just that everyone calls her Granny Mary. She's just been around the place ever since I was young, sort of a ubiquitous granny rather than a specific one. Sorry.'

My face had clearly fallen. I'd thought he was more intimately connected to the life of Patrick, now he was just a passer-by? 'I see,' I said, tightly.

'Oh, but you're right about him needing food, of course. I'll... I'll ask Granny... I mean, I'll ask Mary about it. But, will he be all right to stay until we finish filming? It sounds as though he's going to be an integral part of the storyline.'

Oh, bugger. I was firmly painted into a corner here. Say no to Patrick and it might risk the cottage not being used as a location, and we needed the money. Say yes, and I was stuck with a grazing machine with soup-bowl feet and a penchant for watching me boil the kettle. Plus Poppy's growing attachment to him, which I wasn't keen on.

Gabriel was watching me. I looked at him sideways as we sat amid the fug and chatter. There was a curious kind of stillness about him; he didn't swivel all the time to watch the darts match or people coming and going. He just sat, hands around his pint of cider, as though life was going on around him without touching him at all. My mind briefly contrasted him with Luc, whose sociability and high-functioning boredom meant that he would have joined the darts game, bought a round for everyone in here and started at least three conversations with random strangers before we'd even sat down.

If he'd ever been so pleb as to go into a country pub, of course. Wine bars were more his thing.

I smiled. It felt stretched, as though I was forcing my face. 'This is a nice place.'

He jerked his head in a sideways nod, but it stopped him from looking at me in that curiously concentrated way. 'Noisy. Nearest pub to Steepleton and Landle, so it's usually busy, but the cider is good and local.' Then he swept a hand up and pushed his hair from his face. 'Sorry. Am I staring?'

'No. Well, yes, a bit.'

He gave a rueful smile and looked back down into his drink. 'Sorry. It's...' He took the glasses off and laid them on the table. Without them his face looked less defensive, more classically good-looking, with the curve of cheekbones more pronounced and his eyes a more realistic size. 'Sight's degenerating. Even with these it's not great, and I can't wear them any thicker or I'll topple over.'

I didn't know what to say, so I just sipped my orange juice.

'The location job is a pity posting, y'see.' He picked up his glasses and turned them over between his fingers. 'I'm going to be functionally blind in a few years.' The words were matter-of-fact, but there was emotion quivering behind them. 'So I've got to earn while I can.'

I had no idea what to say to that. Part of me wanted to do what I would have done with Poppy, thrown out ideas, things to be looked into and researched. But the rest of me knew that wasn't what he wanted or needed. This wasn't a problem to be solved, it was a life-altering reality.

'It must be hard.' I hoped I'd injected enough sympathy into my voice.

'Pretty shit, yes,' and the half-laugh in his tone told me I'd done the right thing. 'And I'm telling you just so you know that I'm not being a total bastard about Patrick and the van. I'd help you out with him only, well, I don't know much about horses and I can't see well enough to pick it up on the fly.'

'He needs some hay and a hay net, at the least. Otherwise he's going to start losing condition, and it will be hard to tell under that winter coat he's growing.' I sipped down the last of the orange juice.

'Were you one of those pony-mad children?' He'd left his glasses off, and it was interesting watching eyes that weren't intently fixed on something. He was looking at me directly, yet from what he'd said he couldn't really see my face that well.

'Something like that.' I put my glass down firmly. 'Well, I ought to get back. Poppy is fine left alone for a while, but she's still a bit nervous of the quiet.'

'Poppy's your daughter?'

'Yep. Fourteen and city born and bred. Although I don't much think it matters where they are from, fourteen-year-olds have "attitude" fitted as standard.'

Gabriel smiled. It was a nice smile; it crinkled up those impeccable cheekbones and made him look more approachable. 'There's going to be a fair bit of noise and disruption when we film at your place. How will she cope with that?'

'She will be in her element. Noise and disruption are what she's all about. On her own terms, naturally.'

'Naturally. We were all fourteen once, weren't we?' He put his glass on the table next to mine. 'I'm sorry? Did I say something?'

'No, no...' But the cold finger of memory had stroked its way down my spine like a ghost in this warm, companionable room. 'No, I was just... anyway, I'd better go.'

'I'll walk you to your car.'

He stood up too, tall enough to cause the darts players to shout, 'Oy, shift over, lanky!' when his height intruded on their game.

Although the shout was good-natured, Gabriel did a sort of half-hunch, where most men would probably have raised two fingers and shouted back. He scuttled alongside me out of the pub, where the night air met us clear and chilly. 'Sorry about that.'

'They were just being idiots.' I unlocked my car and we stood beside it for a moment. He looked as though he was weighing up the best way to take his leave. 'Do you need a lift anywhere?'

'A lift?' he asked, as though this was the most bizarre suggestion anyone had ever made.

'Yes, you know, you sit next to me and I drive my car where you need to go. Lift. It's not an abstract concept.' I hoped he'd accept, because I wasn't sure whether I was going to go for the handshake businesslike farewell, or whether a cheek kiss might be more appropriate. Long exposure to Luc and his family, combined with much living in France, had made the cheek-to-cheek double kiss almost automatic, but I had to remind myself that in rural Dorset it probably meant you had to get engaged or something.

He shook his head. The slight, but nippy, breeze was tossing his hair about and he pushed it back with a hand. 'Yes, sorry, I know what you mean, it's just that I'm only a couple of miles from home, and the idea of driving that short a distance is odd.'

'I thought you lived in Bridport?' I remembered him saying something about it not being easy to find Patrick accommodation because of where he lived.

'Well, I do, but I'm staying in Christmas Steepleton while I'm doing this location work. With my sister, Thea – she's got a little flat over her shop. It's easier than coming in every day on the bus.'

'Oh.'

'So, goodbye, then. I'll come over in a couple of days and bring you the contract, show Keenan the place, that sort of thing.'

I sort of held out a hand and went for a cheek kiss simultaneously. He saw me lean in at the same time as his hand went out, and we ended up punching each other in the ribcage whilst banging our heads together as we tried to pull out of the 'kiss' situation without making contact. 'Ow,' I said, although it hadn't been hard enough to hurt.

'Sorry.' Gabriel rubbed his chest. 'That was...'

'Awkward, yes. My fault, too much French kissing. Oh, no, I don't mean that, I mean I've spent a lot of time in France. I teach French. And my husband was French. *Is* French,' I gabbled, trying to cover up the fact that my face was so hot that it was probably summoning help from nearby villages, like a beacon on the cliffs. 'So, yes. Goodbye.'

I got into the car and drove out of the car park with my window wound down to try to cool my cheeks.

6

A few days later, on a wet and windy day that made Dorset seem a bit less charming and a bit more exposed, I drove through to Bournemouth to buy Patrick a hay net. The orchard was getting muddy, except for the patch at the top of the slope, and I began to worry that he wouldn't be getting enough food from the remaining grass.

When I drove back, windscreen wipers flailing ineffectually against the rain, there was a car parked in the gateway. Patrick had his head over the gate and was staring at it as though he'd never seen a wheeled vehicle before, and I had to inch past to get my car to its usual resting place near the front gate.

The rain thundered on the car roof. The lane was practically a stream, water cascading down the hill towards the ford and mingling with the leaves that were starting to fall. The whole thing had become a slick surface of brown, interwoven with little rivulets, like a map of the Nile delta done in miniature outside my door.

As soon as I got out of the car, the doors to the other car

opened and Gabriel and Keenan came dashing out. Gabriel
had his coat collar turned up and Keenan was holding a
macintosh spread out over his head, like a tiny portable tent.

'You should have rung,' I said, opening the front door.
'Said you were coming, and I'd have been in.'

'It's fine.' Keenan dusted rain off the top of his thinning
hair. 'I really wanted to look at the outside anyway, get a feel
for the place, do a bit of logistics work. I think it will be great,
but we'll need a small crew, maybe bring the minibus down.
We won't get the lorries down this lane – in fact, the minibus
might be a squeeze.'

'And Larch won't walk in.' Gabriel was looking around at the
walls now. With the recent drop in temperature and increase in
humidity, they'd assumed a kind of slickness that the woodlice
were using to stage team luge competitions. 'We might have to
form a human chain to carry her down from the main road.'

Keenan sighed. 'Yeah, for a nature lover, she really doesn't
like being outside much, does she?'

'Or getting wet, getting cold, wind, too much sunshine,
noisy seagulls and most other wildlife. Are we actually sure
that it's nature she likes and not just photographs of fields?'

Gabriel gave me a sideways grin and I realised that I was
being included in this insider talk for a reason. It was an
introduction to the cast in a roundabout way, presumably so
that I wouldn't be all star-struck and breathless when I met
them.

He needn't have bothered. I'd met famous people before
and, essentially, they were mostly just wallies who were good
at one particular thing. Actors wouldn't be any different, just
better looking.

'So, can I have a tour?' Keenan carefully draped the wet

raincoat over the back of a chair. I'd led them through to the kitchen, which was marginally warmer than the rest of the house, although the damp air clung more in here. The flag-stones shone with the water, and condensation was making little net curtains over the windows.

'Of course. Gabriel, I've ordered some hay for Patrick. They're going to deliver it tomorrow. You might want to tell... Granny Mary.' It felt awkward, giving a personalised name to a woman I'd never met, although, the way Gabriel used it, it was more as if Granny Mary were her actual name than an honorific.

'Good thinking. I'll text her later. I'm going over to see her tomorrow, so, no doubt, she'll have things to tell me then. I think she's been quite worried about Patrick, so it will be a relief.'

'How is she doing?' I put the kettle on the stove. Keenan was lurking about in the doorway as though he was trying to urge me on with the house tour. I couldn't really blame him – until the stove really got going it was a bit like being at the bottom of a well in here.

'She's coming on nicely. Thank you.'

'And Patrick is the horse?' Keenan asked, still hovering.

'Yes. He's just out there.' I pointed to the streaming window.

Keenan looked towards it and jumped back with a little scream. 'Oh, dear God, it's like something out of a horror film!'

Patrick had his nose right up against the window and was looking in with his pirate eye. He blew a long snort, which sent a spray up the glass, and then shook himself impres-sively. He'd got a full winter coat now, which made him look twice as wide, and a series of muddy patches where he'd been rolling under the trees.

'Are you sure that's a horse? It's not a cow doing impressions?' Keenan asked, with nervous apprehension in every word. 'Because I'm beginning to think the pig idea was maybe better.'

'He's fine,' I said, leading Keenan off to show him the rest of the house. As I ushered him through the depressingly short series of rooms, I realised that I'd actually grown quite fond of Patrick. Although probably in the same way as one would grow fond of an occasional stalker, or a nasty fungal infection – they were a presence that you got used to.

'And that's pretty much Harvest Cottage.' I concluded the tour with us traipsing back down the still bare-floored staircase, our footsteps rattling in competition with the rain on the roof.

Keenan bit his lip. 'You're right, Gabe!' he called. 'Pretty much has serial killer written all over it.'

'Thanks,' I muttered. 'I do have to live here, you know.'

Gabriel came out of the kitchen with mugs. 'The kettle boiled,' he said. 'I don't know how you take yours, but I assumed some milk and sugar wouldn't go amiss in this atmosphere. It's like camping, indoors.'

I almost dropped the mug in surprise. How long had it been since someone made me a cup of tea? Luc would never have thought of it, and he despised ordinary tea. If it wasn't coffee strong enough to keep the shape of the cup as you drank it, or one of the million different forms of Earl Grey that Harrods Food Hall sold, he wasn't interested. Poppy would sometimes offer, but usually forget and go off to do something more interesting than pander to her aged parent's tea urge. Work then, probably. Basia would sometimes make a cup for both of us, if I was deep in conversation with the department head, but we usually made our own in the staffroom.

Even though I usually took my tea with a tiny splash of milk and no sugar, I drank Gabriel's tea as though it were the nectar of the gods. And he was right: the touch of sugar helped my mood to lift beyond the heavy clouds and persistent rain.

'Next week all right?' Keenan looked at me over the rim of his mug. The steam from the tea had made his glasses steam up, and I noticed that Gabriel had taken his off, probably for just that reason. 'Weather forecast is better for next week. We'll do Larch's scenes first. We'll carry her in in a sedan chair if we have to, but we'll never get her down here if it's raining. We've got to make the most of Peter while we've got him too. He's off doing a *Broadchurch* docu soon, so we have to fit his scenes in.'

I had no idea who 'Peter' was, and probably didn't need to know. 'Do you need me to be around?' I asked.

Keenan and Gabriel exchanged a look. 'We-e-e-e-elll...' Keenan pushed at his glasses. 'If you promise not to be one of those home-owners who say, "Mind the china!" and, "You can't go in there!" as we try to set up shots...'

'I haven't got any china except these mugs and a couple of plates,' I said, waving a hand to indicate the kitchen. 'And you've got free run of the place – you're paying for it, after all. You *are* still paying, aren't you?' I added, with an anxious look at the electricity meter on the wall, which was ticking away the fact that I'd put all the lights on to make the place look more inviting. It actually just made it look like a well-illuminated serial-killer hideout, evidently.

'Yeah, course. Finance will be on it now.'

I tried to hide my relief, but I think Gabriel noticed. He must have been really good at reading big-picture body language, because my face wasn't close enough for him to see my expression, even though he'd put his glasses back on. After our disturbingly uncomfortable parting the other night, I didn't want to stand too close to him. He probably winced as an automatic reaction whenever I approached anyway.

'I'm going to take a look outside.' Keenan pulled his macintosh from the back of the chair, where it had dripped little puddles onto the floor. 'I want to get a proper vision of the front, maybe go down to the ford and see what it's like down there.'

'Knock yourself out.' Gabriel perched on the corner of the kitchen table. 'I'm staying in the dry. Well, dryish,' he corrected, looking at the wall near the pantry, where a now-visible skin of damp was forming. 'This is only not outdoors because convention dictates.'

I gave him a probably wasted stern look. 'We can't all afford double-glazed centrally heated comfort, you know,' I said. 'Poppy and I have a roof over our heads and we're grateful for that. Well, *I'm* grateful, she complains constantly, but that's pretty much standard for fourteen. If you don't live in a palace with servants to clean, pick up after you and do your homework for you, then life isn't, apparently, worth living.' I thought for a moment. 'Actually, even if you have all those things, life is pretty shit when you're fourteen.'

'Didn't you say you were a pony-mad girl? Fourteen is about prime age for spending every possible moment in the stable, if I remember Thea at that age.' Gabriel sipped more tea. 'I was more about swimming when I was fourteen. School had a swimming team.' His expression went a bit misty. 'Wasn't bad at it either.'

'Yes, well.' I put my mug down so firmly onto the marble slab of the worktop that there was an ominous cracking noise. 'Let's not start wandering down memory lane just now. Patrick needs water.'

The big piebald head had vanished from the window, but there was a heavy squelching sort of noise from outside, which indicated that he was walking round the cottage.

'Water? He's practically swimming out there.'

'But he can't drink it, can he?' I fetched the multi-purpose bucket from the corner, where washing down the paintwork had become a little superfluous – it was currently washing *itself* down perfectly adequately – and tipped it into the sink.

'Would you like to come and meet Granny Mary?' Gabriel asked suddenly. 'I feel she's slightly become the spectre at the feast here, and I know she'd like to meet the person who's taking care of her beloved. You could come with me when I go in tomorrow.'

I hesitated, bucket under the tap.

'It's okay, she doesn't eat people.' Gabriel saw my hesitation. 'At least, not any more.'

And it suddenly came home to me how isolated I'd become. Apart from Gabriel and Keenan and, of course, Poppy, the only conversation I'd really had in the last week had been with the girl behind the till in the equestrian supply shop, who'd sold me the hay net. And *that* had been about the weather. What was happening to me? In London I'd been sociable. I'd talked all day at work, to my students, to my friends, to other staff members. And, of course, to Poppy, although, now I came to think of it, a lot of that talk had been me nagging her to do things.

Was I in danger of becoming a recluse? Tucked away in my little cottage halfway down this hillside, no passing traffic and no drop-in visitors? Well, that was an alarming thought, and it made me answer Gabriel a little reflexively.

'I'd love to meet her. Of course.'

He hesitated. 'We'd need to get the early bus – would that be all right? After ten it's full of bus pass people and you can't always get on.'

I stared at him. 'I can drive, you know.'

'Well, yes, but I didn't like to assume that you—'

'When's visiting time?'

He rubbed a hand through his hair. It seemed to be something he did when he was thinking, I noticed, distracted by how long his hair was. It nearly brushed his collarbone, and I wondered why he'd grown it. 'Eleven, tomorrow.'

'I'll pick you up in the village, then. Half past ten?' Again the hesitancy. Surely he didn't have a thing about women driving? Okay, this was rural Dorset, but it wasn't backwoods America, and he looked fairly evolved.

'Are you sure it's no trouble?' He'd taken the glasses off again now, and was looking at me with that curiously exposed look that glasses wearers often have when they have their barrier against the world removed.

'Compared to finding a bus stop, waiting, missing the bus, bus running late, getting to the other end and having to find the location whilst not knowing where to get the bus back from? I'd say driving was the least of it.'

Gabriel tilted his head. 'Some of us don't have a choice,' he said gently.

'Sorry, no. Of course. But I don't mind driving and the car could do with being out a bit more often. It's starting to look like the world's most expensive garden gnome out there.'

I didn't know whether it was my apology or my lightening of the tone, but his face lightened too. 'Tomorrow at ten thirty.

I'll be outside Thea's shop waiting. You can't miss it – it's the one with all the knitted monstrosities in the window. Now I'd better go and syphon Kee back into the car. We've got to see a couple more locations this afternoon before it gets dark.'

We stood together in the doorway. Keenan was a dark smear beyond the window; he'd wound his coat around his upper body and head like a shroud and was walking up and down the front path, glazed with rain and muttering.

'Looks like Davin's family banshee on holiday,' Gabriel observed. 'Let me get him out of here.'

We stared at one another for a moment. 'Let's agree on a handshake,' I said.

'I was going to go for cheek kiss?'

'I'm just going to gently pat your arm. It's safer.'

There was a bit of a moment of confusion when we both raised our right hands, but because we were standing face to face there wasn't room for either of us to do anything with the raised hand, and we lowered them again.

'Take it as read?' he said, after a bit of elbow-clonking.

'I think so, yes.' I opened the door.

Keenan, mac over head dripping like a gutter, jumped and then said, 'We'd better go. I think I'm dissolving.'

I closed the door and went back to Patrick's bucket.

7

The rain had stopped when I woke up the next morning. I knew it was late from the way the sun was inching its way up over the breast of the hill, and sat up in a panic.

'Poppy! You'll be late for school! Are you up?'

There was no reply. Maybe she'd managed to get up, get ready for school and leave for the bus without waking me? I laughed at my delusion. Poppy hadn't managed to do *anything* silently since she was about seven; every movement was accompanied with either music blaring or heavy footsteps and sighing. I pulled a dressing gown on over my pyjamas. It had been a cool night and the sun's edges had definite over-tones of crispness about them.

No sign of her in the house, and the back door was wide open. I stuck my head outside and felt the cold grip of horror constrict my throat.

'What the *hell* are you doing?'

I was hardly even aware of what *I* was doing and my vision had narrowed to a sliver through my lashes. All I could focus on was Poppy sitting, perched up on Patrick's wide back, reading a book. She was lolling sideways, the book resting on his scrubby withers, whilst he grazed absolutely unconcerned, stepping carefully around a huge puddle that had accumulated yesterday in the middle of the field.

'Get down now!' I had to have two goes at getting the words out – my mouth was sticky and my tongue dry as a feather.

Poppy looked up from her book. Patrick raised his head briefly, snorted, and went back to the grass. 'Why?'

The 'because I say so' response had been eliminated from my toolbox of parental equipment a long time ago, by the series of 'why?'s that always resulted, so I had to think fast. 'Because it's not safe!'

Something in my tone, or the fact that I'd run out in only my slippers across the wet grass and mud, was clearly convincing because she sighed and slid down, landing her booted feet alongside Patrick's huge ones. He shook himself and wandered off. 'Wow, overreaction much? It's not fair. I've got this pony and I can't even *sit* on him? Dad says—'

'I am so uninterested in what your father says that I am practically comatose about it.' Relief heated my veins. 'Patrick is – well, he might not even be broken to ride, and anything could have startled him.'

We both looked at the stolid fourteen hands of eating machine, ripping grass from under the big apple tree with his teeth and a noise like a hundred plasters being removed at once. Anything less likely to be flighty and easily startled it was hard to imagine. He had all the capriciousness of a tonne of wet concrete.

'You are *not* to sit on him again.' The hot wet flood of relief through my veins made my words sharper than was wise.

Poppy rolled her eyes and did the deep shrug that meant

she'd taken my words on board and they'd last as long as it took her to work out an argument against them. It was no good. Patrick would have to go. I couldn't risk her doing this sort of thing again; not when anything could happen. A bird could fly out of a hedge, startle the pony, and then she'd be thrown... 'And why aren't you at school?'

She started her dismal stomp towards the front door, and barely hesitated. 'Because it's *Saturday*, Mum, and even those slave drivers don't make us go in on a Saturday.' A hesitation in her step. 'Mum...' There was a tone of concerned affection in the word, which meant she wanted something.

'What?' I tried not to sound sarcastic. She'd got off Patrick, the danger was over, and I needed to keep her onside about this. Any kind of annoyance would increase the stomp.

'Please would you drop me over in Steepleton in a bit? Rory and I are going to hang out and he's going to talk to his mum about me getting a job waitressing in her café, that's not in Steepleton it's a couple of bays over but she works for the catering van sometimes and Rory said he can introduce me to Davin O'Riordan if he's there and we can hang out on the beach with the dogs.' A pause for breath and she tilted her head to one side, for a moment looking so much like her father that it made me grind my teeth. 'Is that all right?'

'As it happens, yes, I'm going over to Steepleton to pick up Gabriel and visit Patrick's owner in the hospital.'

'I'll get changed, then. Oh, and you can ask if Patrick can be ridden, can't you? While you're there?'

'No,' I said to her retreating back. And then, discovering that it was nearly nine o'clock, I panicked and dashed upstairs to try and beat her to the bathroom.

* * *

I dropped Poppy off at the turning circle between the beach and the harbour. Clearly it was a fate worse than death to be seen arriving with one's mother, although since Rory knew she was fourteen I didn't know why – did he imagine she'd drive herself? Poppy leaped from the car almost before I'd stopped and with a, 'Thanks, Mum,' and a slammed door she was gone, hair flying. She was wearing quite a lot of make-up too, I'd noticed. She must have been watching those YouTube tutorials again, because she'd had fat, drawn-on eyebrows and dark streaks of 'contouring' under each cheekbone. I knew better than to say anything, but the whole look was reminiscent of someone who'd fallen asleep in the vicinity of a four-year-old with crayons.

Fourteen. It was a hell of an age.

I parked the car between two vans, one with spools of wiring spilling from the side and a group of people standing about kicking at the wires, talking and pointing. An area of the nearby beach was taped off and empty, apart from a small wiry dog, which was dashing up and down with a piece of seaweed in its mouth.

The wind off the sea was cold. It held the tang of promised winter, and scuttered crisp packets and bronze leaves up and down the road as I walked up to the little row of shops that overlooked the sand.

'Hello.' Gabriel had been leaning against a wall outside the first shop, one leg up behind him on a rail and a long black coat billowing with the wind. 'Good timing.'

He turned and gave a thumbs up to whoever was in the shop. When I peered through the window, which was heavily overhung with crocheted sea-scenes, I saw a young woman in multicoloured dungarees peering out. We looked awkwardly at one another for a moment, then she turned away to rearrange a series of knitted fish and a huge carved seagull on a shelf. 'That's my sister, Thea.'

'Does she make all those things?' I wanted to add, 'And if so, *why*?' but reasoned that, just because I couldn't see the need for knitted haddock and crocheted postcards, didn't mean they didn't sell well.

'Yeah.' He unhooked his leg. 'If you can make it out of wool, then Thea will make it. I suspect she's started trying to weave herself a boyfriend in the back room. That loom is altogether too reminiscent of the three Fates; if she's not careful she'll start cackling and calling people "my pretty". Sorry.' He pushed at his glasses as the wind left his coat alone and started on his hair. 'I'm a bit jaded.'

'Preaching to the choir, mate,' I muttered. 'Shall we go?'

* * *

Bridport hospital was more modern-looking than I'd expected from an aspiring chocolate-box town. Inside it smelled as all hospitals do, of boiled sheets and industrial-strength cleaner. I followed Gabriel along corridors clustered with people standing chatting in varying degrees of clothing, some dragging IV stands, up two floors in the lift and on to G ward. I didn't like to ask if the G was for 'General' or 'Geriatric'; it wasn't easy to tell from the occupants.

He led me down to a small bay right at the end of the ward, where big windows let a more normal light into the room, relegating the overhead lights to second place. 'Hello, Granny Mary. This is Katie, who's looking after Patrick for us.'

He didn't raise his voice in a 'talking to the hard of hearing' way, nor slow his words as I noticed a lot of people doing when they talked to the elderly. It made me like him, in a curious way.

Granny Mary was sitting in a chair by the window. She was not at all what I'd been expecting, even though I wasn't quite sure what I *had* been expecting. A little old lady, possibly, hunched, grey hair, bed jacket, a bit *Little Red Riding Hood's* grandma, pre wolf-ingestion. This lady had streaked auburn and blonde hair, an AC/DC T-shirt, and was typing furiously on her mobile phone.

'Oh, hi, Gabe,' she said, giving me a mother-in-law of a look. 'I'd forgotten you were coming. Well, how's my beast doing?'

As this was addressed to me, I assumed she meant Patrick. If she meant Gabriel, then I really did not know how to answer, so I took the path of least resistance. 'Patrick's fine. I've got some hay in for him because there's not a lot of grass left in the orchard. But he's really going to have to go somewhere else, I'm afraid.' I tried to inject the right amount of urgency without upsetting her. 'My daughter was sitting on him today, and I really can't let that happen.'

'Gabe, pop down to the shop and get me a magazine, would you?' Granny Mary moved her acid blue eyes to Gabriel, without acknowledging me. 'A proper one, I mean, not one of those with celebrity boobs on. I've seen enough tits over my lifetime to last me.'

Gabriel gave me a kind of sideways smile and a half-wink, and headed off out of the ward, leaving me with the frankly terrifying prospect of Granny Mary, who turned her eyes onto me with a force that obliterated everything else in the ward. I'd never been frightened of an eyeball before – well, all right, maybe once, in dissection class in Year Ten when Andrew

Waites had done the whole 'look at this' routine – but Granny Mary had eyes that could cut metal.

I shifted about a bit. I didn't want to sit on the bed, she was in the only chair, and standing in front of her was like being confronted by the worst headmistress in the world. I put my hands in my pockets, then took them out again, while those blue lenses gave me the disconcerting feeling that she was looking into my soul. 'Er,' I said.

'You were Katherine Bryant,' Granny Mary said eventually. 'I know about what happened.'

Even though the ward was warm, a current of cold air hit me somewhere around the back of my neck. It didn't just come from the fact that she'd picked up on my past life, but the feeling that she'd somehow managed to look inside my head, pick out my worst secrets using some kind of magic. It was creepy and, coming from a lady who looked less gypsy and more like a particularly stringent auditor, oddly disconnected.

I opened my mouth, then closed it. Then, eventually, because I had to ask, 'Do you have a crystal ball?'

She tutted and rolled her eyes. 'No.' She lifted her phone and shook it at me. 'Google.'

'Oh.' I wasn't sure if that made it better or worse.

'When Gabe told me about you looking after Patrick, he sent me some pictures. You were in one, and, whatever you think of me, I won't just leave my pony with anyone, so I looked you up.' She gave me another appraising look. 'You've put on weight.'

'Okay.' The insult made me feel better. 'Yes, all right, that's who I *was*, but it's not who I am now, and I'd appreciate you keeping it to yourself.'

Those eyes were like a laser, I was surprised she hadn't

scorched her eyebrows off. 'Would you, now? And why would that be? Got yourself set on our Gabe, have you, and worried that he might be put off?'

This was so far from the truth that it made me take a step back, where I connected with the metal frame of the bed. '*What?* No! Of course not.'

She sniffed and turned her glare away from me and out of the window again. 'Don't know why not. He's a nice boy. Only one to turn out and help me in my hour of need.' She shook the phone again. 'I've got most of Steepleton in here, and it's only really him and his sister that bother with me.'

I caught myself before I said, 'How surprising, what with you being the very embodiment of charm and pleasantness.' I'd trained up on my mother, and knew how pointless it would be.

'Mind you, Thea's got a brain that's ninety per cent wool.'

'Anyway.' I tried to get us back on track. 'We're going to have to move Patrick. Like I said, my daughter was sitting on him this morning and—'

'Patrick won't hurt her,' Granny Mary said, very definitely. 'He's ride and drive. I don't ride any more these days, but you could stick a saddle on that beast and take him across country any day of the week. He's *obliging*, is Patrick.'

I had a brief mental image of the rotund barrel shape of Patrick hurtling around the countryside and jumping obstacles. As long as those obstacles came no higher than his knees and you could find a saddle that would fit, and you didn't go fast or for longer than five minutes, she was probably right. 'That's beside the point,' I said, sharply. 'The fact is that I don't want my daughter sitting on him, and he's eaten most of the grass and he's poaching up the little orchard into mud.'

Granny Mary, still looking out of the window, shrugged.

'He's used to poor grazing,' she said. 'Get him some feed in. Gabe knows my bank details, get him to transfer you some money. Patrick will be fine. He's never been rugged up in his life, and there's enough shelter under those old apple trees.'

'But—' I began.

'And Gabe was saying that they might be using him in this detective series they're filming. That'll be nice, seeing Patrick on the TV.' She spoke comfortably, as though this was a done deal, and I took another step backwards, which sat me on the edge of the bed, as though my legs had been swept from underneath me physically as well as mentally.

The metallic eyes rested on me again. There was a slight relaxation to the eyebrows that might have been amusement. 'Got you over a bit of a barrel here, haven't we?' she observed. 'You need the money from them filming at your place, and they'll only film if you keep Patrick.'

'Yes, thank you for pointing that out.' I tried to think. Well, at least I could charge her for the hay and the hay net. I'd been a bit worried I was going to be picking up the bill for Patrick's increasing winter appetite.

'I wouldn't have put him in there when I felt *this* coming on—' Granny Mary waved a hand at her head '—if I didn't think he'd be safe. And the van, is the van all right?'

'We put it in the orchard too,' I said, a bit weakly.

'Good. Got to watch out – there's always someone wants a poke about inside. Don't know why. It's like they think we're hobbits or something, just cos we live in a little space. People buy places that are far too big. All you need is a bed, a cooker and somewhere to wash, not all this fancy "utility room" gubbins and suchlike.'

I refrained from mentioning that a working toilet was also desirable. I hadn't got to grips with what she'd been doing for lavatorial facilities in the caravan, and wasn't sure I wanted to know.

To my utter relief, a confusion at the ward entrance brought Gabriel back in, bearing a copy of *New Scientist* and a *Horse & Hound*. 'Wasn't sure what you felt like reading,' he said, slightly breathless as though he'd hurried, which made me like him even more. He wasn't immune to the Granny Mary effect, and knew that she'd be using it on me, it seemed. 'So, I got both.'

'Good lad,' she said, equably.

'Any idea when they're letting you out?' I asked, trying to sound neutral and not at all 'when can I expect your pony gone from my orchard?'.

'Oh, they're not hurrying.' She took the *New Scientist* and flipped to the back pages. 'It was a minor stroke, they reckon, but they want to make sure that there's no long-lasting effects.'

'Oh.'

Gabriel nudged me and, when I looked at him, he twitched his head towards the door and, sod liking him, I practically fell on him with kisses of gratitude. 'We don't want to tire you out,' he said, 'so we'll be off.'

'Right-oh,' said Granny Mary, without looking up. 'Just text if there's a problem. And see that this young lady gets reimbursed for Patrick's expenses.' And that cold, bright stare came up to focus on me again, like a sudden frost. 'She seems concerned about money.'

I wanted to say that I was more concerned for Patrick's welfare, and opened my mouth to argue, but Gabriel bundled me off the ward and back out to the car park before I could respond.

We didn't speak until we were out in the fresh air, standing either side of the car, with the reassuring hiss of traffic passing. It had rained while we were in the hospital, but now the sun had emerged and was laying a thin layer of gold across everything.

'She can be a bit... abrasive,' he said, cautiously, at last. 'You did well.'

'She—' I absolutely wasn't going to mention the conversation we'd had after he left. 'She cares a lot about Patrick.' I unlocked the doors and we got in, as another squally cloud blocked the sun and sent spatters of rain over the car park. 'But you're right, she's a little bit combative, isn't she?'

'Comes from the lifestyle, I suppose.'

I looked sideways at him as I waited to come out of the car park. He was wearing black jeans and a black jacket under a long black coat. Dark hair, dark eyes, even the rims of his glasses were black tinted, and his boots were the practical, heavy kind with the minimum of ornamentation. He looked as though he was trying to slide through the cracks in the world. 'So, what's your lifestyle?' I tried to make the question sound light. 'You're rocking the half-hearted Goth thing quite hard.'

'Am I?' He looked down at the sleeve of his coat as though it were personally responsible for making him look as though he attended every gig My Chemical Romance ever gave. 'I don't think I have a lifestyle. I've never really thought about it.'

'You wear black and your hair is long,' I pointed out. 'Both choices, unless you are a size in which clothing is only available in a single colour and you're allergic to hairdressers.'

He frowned. 'I dunno,' he said, after a moment. 'Nobody really looks at me, so I guess it doesn't matter.'

I looked at him out of the corner of my eye as I swung the car out along the road back towards Christmas Steepleton. Maybe he genuinely didn't know how good-looking he was? But he must be second-glanced by practically every straight woman who walked past him, surely that gave him a bit of a clue? Or did he just think that people customarily hesitated when they walked? Or, even worse, was he disingenuously trying to make me feel sorry for him in some kind of way? Because that was bloody ridiculous.

'I'm sure you've had your share of being ogled,' I said, somewhat tartly. Living with a high-drama fourteen-year-old gave me a limited supply of patience for self-pity.

'I've had my share of *relationships*,' he replied. 'Not necessarily being ogled.'

'So you aren't currently attached?' I was just making conversation, but Granny Mary's words about having my eye on him suddenly came back to me and sent blood pounding into my cheeks so hard that I really didn't need the indicator to show I was turning right, the whole of the inside of the car was probably illuminated. 'Er, I mean...'

He shifted, straightening out the coat. 'Currently, no,' he said, heavily. 'Oddly enough, women seem to want a man who can see further than the end of his eyelashes, who's working on a career and who doesn't—' he turned to face me suddenly '—dress like a Victorian who's recently lost a close relative.'

'Sorry,' I muttered.

He sighed and took his glasses off. Cupped his face in his hands and took a deep breath. 'I wear black,' he said, quietly, 'because then everything matches. I don't have great colour vision unless I use a magnifying glass, and it's hard to tell the difference between everything toning and looking okay, and going out looking like a David Bowie poster. Thea's idea. Stick to one colour, makes life easier.'

I felt awful. I gave myself a quick, silent talking-to for my snap judgement-making.

He turned his head so he was looking out of the passenger window and I couldn't see his face, only the dark drift of hair that fell over the collar of his coat. 'There's still a lot of traditional expectations of men,' he said, evenly. 'Okay, we might not be looked on as the sole breadwinner any more, there's more equality in relationships, but, when it comes down to it, a lot of women want a man who's on the up. I'm slowly going blind. There's no way of knowing how much functional vision I'll have left, so—' I saw his hand, resting along his leg, curl into a loose fist and relax. 'Yeah. Damaged goods.'

Damaged goods. Yes. I knew how that felt.

'But...' I was going to launch into some kind of diatribe against shallowness, then reminded myself that his looks were the first thing I'd noticed about him so I wasn't really in a position to comment about superficiality. Besides, living with a fourteen-year-old gave a whole new insight into exactly how phoney people could be, although teenagers weren't truly 'people' yet, more 'humans in training'. 'I'm sorry,' I said, eventually. 'It must be tough.'

He didn't answer and kept his face averted. We bumped off the main road down the turning towards Steepleton, the hedges drawing in around us as the lanes narrowed. A filmy curtain of rain came down, glazing the road and making the wipers squeal across the windscreen.

'Great. More rain,' I said, more for something to say than as a meteorological observance.

'Dorset in the autumn. It's why the cliffs are eroding so fast – they're getting it from below and above and they're mostly made of prehistoric mud in the first place.' His lightness of tone reassured me that he hadn't taken extreme umbrage at my foot-in-mouth moments over his disability. 'Two really good storms and your cottage will be a mile closer to the beach.'

I shivered. The thought that nature could do that, just wipe out acres of land, and the thought of my little cottage sitting on the edge of a sliding cliff, gave me the creeps. I realised I'd got quite fond of the damp, mildewy place.

We jolted down the hill towards Steepleton. Far in the distance through the rain curtains, I could see the restless grey corpse of the sea and, for the first time, it felt like coming home. A couple of fishing boats were stapled to the skyline, stationary at this distance, and I felt a tiny knot of tension between my shoulder blades begin to unravel.

'Mum!' Poppy bounced up to the car as soon as I stopped. She'd dropped the over-sophisticated air she'd had when I left her and become more like a child from Enid Blyton, with her hair piled up on her head and tied with some left-over tape, and her clothes tugged by the breeze. 'This is Rory. Can I stay here for the rest of the day? We're going to walk over the cliffs and see his mum and I've met Davin O'Riordan and *he* said we can take his dogs for a walk.'

Behind her, hovering uncertainly, was a gangly boy with a ridiculous haircut. He had wide brown eyes and an appealing dash of freckles and looked as though meeting me was the single most terrifying thing that had ever happened to him.

I glanced at Gabriel, who was smiling to himself. 'Hello, Rory, nice to meet you. Yes, you can stay, but keep your phone on.'

Rory grinned. 'Hi, Gabe,' then gave me an uncertain smile. 'Neil can drive her back later, if you like,' he said, diffidently, shrugging himself deeper into a fluorescent jacket that had CREW written on it.

'Oh, yes, and I can show Rory Patrick!' Poppy was filled with the inner brightness of a combination of crush, hero-worship, new surroundings and the prospect of showing off. 'He's our pony,' she finished.

'Yes, heard Granny Mary left her horse in your field,' said Rory, who clearly had not yet heard the phrase 'buzz-kill'.

Poppy subsided a couple of centimetres, but then revived. 'Shall we go and pick up Davin's dogs, then? See you, Mum.' And, with the briefest of incurious glances thrown at Gabriel, she seized Rory's arm and dragged him away.

His cry of, 'Nice to meet you!' was borne away on the rising wind. Gabriel and I sat for a moment, sapped by the relentless energy of the young.

'Would you like a coffee?' he asked, at last. 'There's a little café just up the main street – don't know if you've discovered it yet. And I should buy you a drink for driving me all the way out to Bridport.'

Half of me wanted to decline and head back to the clammy cottage. But the other half of me was doing a Poppy, jumping up and down and asking what the point was of going back, when I couldn't do any more to the cottage because of film reasons, and besides it was chilly and dank and this man was really quite cute and I needed more company that wasn't an equine damply squelching around outside.

'That sounds nice,' I said brightly, and got out.

'You don't have to overdo the enthusiasm,' Gabriel said.

'If it's a choice between coffee in a warm place, hell, warm *coffee*, and sitting around in the heat sink that is my cottage, while the invertebrates play kiss chase on the walls, I think I'll take the coffee,' I said, somewhat stung by his assumption that my eagerness was fake.

He stopped for a second. Just a momentary halt in closing the car door, but it was a hesitation in movement that I noticed. 'I'm sorry,' he said, quietly.

'What for?' I found myself very concerned with my car keys to avoid looking at his face. When I did glance at it, there was an expression I couldn't read, something complicated and dark.

'My sister's always telling me to stop it with the self-pity. Sometimes I just genuinely don't see – no pun intended, sorry. I get so wrapped up in myself, in the not knowing what's going to happen, how bad it's going to get, my own troubles, basically, that I forget everyone else has problems too.' He held out a hand. 'I'm a bit of a twunt sometimes, and having a disability does not excuse me. Sorry.'

I looked at his hand, then reached out slowly to take it. We shook hands. His skin was warm, his fingers long and careful around mine. 'You heretofore have my permission to clout me a good 'un if I get all "I am the only person to suffer" again, okay?'

'Can I use foreign objects? To clout you?' I tried to sound light and jokey, but the inside of my mouth had gone a bit sticky. I realised this was the first time I'd properly touched a man since Luc. Okay, it was a handshake, not intercourse, but there was something intimate about that skin-to-skin contact and those fingers cupping my hand.

'Up to, and including, loose bits of cardboard. No woks,' he said. 'Oh. Sorry again, for all I know you've been a domestic violence victim and I've just made light of – look, this is all going a bit pear-shaped, shall I shut up now?'

We slowly disentangled hands and turned our backs to the wind to walk up the slope towards coffee. 'No violence,' I said at last, quietly. 'Luc never hit me.'

Gabriel twitched his head in my direction. 'He's a bit abrasive though, isn't he? I mean, I could hear him, even through all the blood and the layers of tea towel – he's used to getting his own way.'

'He's French,' I said, and then realised that that didn't explain anything. 'No, that's not fair. He grew up with an immense amount of privilege, his family own loads of vineyards and chateaux and stuff. He's a little bit divorced from real life. And me, now, obviously.' I grabbed the metal rail that ran up the middle of the road that ran vertiginously up the hillside. Another squall of grey rain blew through, dashing up the hill ahead of us. 'He's not a bad man. He just really wasn't cut out for marriage and parenthood and all that, and we were too young when we got together to realise it. But I've got Poppy, and I wouldn't have anything any different. Except,' I thought, drawn to introspection by the gradient, 'maybe a better heating system.'

'What about you?' Gabriel paused. He'd got ahead of me, clearly more used to scaling the heights of Steepleton than I was.

'My mum was widowed when I was young. I grew up in London.' This didn't really answer his question and I knew it, but I really didn't want him raking over my upbringing. 'Boring, really.'

'My sister and I grew up here.' Gabriel stopped again and turned. 'Mum's got a B&B further up the hill and Dad used to fish until he started helping her in the business. It's not such a bad place, once you get used to the hill and the wind. And if you like mackerel.'

We'd stopped outside the coffee shop that also seemed, inexplicably, to be an estate agency. A plate of scones nestled in the window alongside the property details of a house halfway to Dorchester and a sun-faded request for EXTRAS FOR FILMING. An ice cream wrapper accelerated up the hill past us on the stiff breeze and the air smelled of old seaweed and rain on ancient tarmac. Apart from the distant voices, the shushing of the sea and the howl of the wind past my ears, it was quiet.

'Yes,' I said, and then, more strongly, 'yes. I'm getting used to it.'

Gabriel led the way into the café and went to sit at a table. I wasn't sure if he wanted me to order at the counter, or whether it was table service, so I sort of hovered for a moment.

'Hi, Gabe.' There was a woman sitting at a desk in the other half of the room. 'D'you want coffee?' When she stood up I saw she was wearing the jacket and skirt uniform and name tag of the estate agent, and the apron of the waitress.

'Two coffees, please, Maisy.' He sprawled himself out in the seat, clearly comfortable with his surroundings.

The woman, keeping her eyes on me at all times as though I were about to go off like a hand grenade, shuffled around behind the counter and began pouring coffee into two tall mugs. 'You keeping all right, then, Gabe?' She was still watching me. Her gaze was fifty per cent judgement and fifty per cent suspicion, but that was fine. The city had trained me up on people judging me and my past had made me used to suspicion. I gave her a broad smile as she brought the coffee over; she had nothing to fear from me.

'Pretty much. You all right?' Gabriel addressed her with the ease of long association. 'Dad all right? How are the boys?'

'Ah, we're going on fine.' Two mugs arrived on the table. 'This your friend, is it?'

Gabriel settled himself more comfortably in the chair. 'This is Katie Gerauld. Harvest Cottage.'

'Oh, ah.' Her face became more animated. 'How you finding it? Took us a while to sell that place, it did.'

I smiled up at her. 'It's lovely. Just right for me and my daughter.'

A laugh which, in London, would have been described as 'tinkly'. 'Not worried by the ghosts, then? I thought you was brave, taking it on when you takes into account its history, but then—' she gave me a quick look up and down '—I s'pose if you're into them arcane practices it's just the right kind of place for that stuff, isn't it?'

'Maisy,' Gabriel said in a warning kind of way.

I wasn't quite sure what she meant by 'arcane practices'. Or by the look. I was wearing jeans and a jumper and looked about as arcane as a brick. The only possibly esoteric things about me were my dangly earrings, which had a slight hint of 'pentagram' about them. They'd been a Christmas present from Poppy, who'd been going through her 'Wiccan' phase at the time.

'I'm pretty sure Harvest Cottage isn't haunted,' I said. 'Unless about a billion generations of slugs have left their mark, and I can't see them doing much more than rattling the odd pot scourer in the sink.'

Maisy's eyes widened. 'They didn't tell you about old Mr Coombes? It was his cottage, and he died in there and they didn't find him for *weeks*!'

'Are you a very successful estate agent?' I asked. 'Only that sort of information is a wee bit off-putting.'

'Maisy,' Gabriel said again. 'Katie's already bought the

place. She lives there. With her daughter. You telling these stories really isn't helpful.' He lifted his mug and turned to me. 'Maisy and I were at school together, where she excelled in creative writing, as you can probably tell.'

Maisy shrugged. 'Just thought she should know people say her place is haunted. If you goes up there late of a night, there's mysterious noises and all sorts.'

'There's mysterious noises *everywhere*,' he said, with a small amount of exasperation leaking out around the edges of his words. 'This is Dorset. Between the hedgehogs mating and the foxes shrieking and those bloody birds that make that whistling sound, even just the wildlife makes such a bloody racket it's surprising that anyone can hear themselves think. Add in a bit of human expectation and some bits of plastic caught in a hedge – well. It's just imagination and stories, Maisy, as you well know.' Two swallows of coffee. 'And it was two *days* before they found Alf Coombes, not weeks.' He addressed me over the mug rim. 'Milkman noticed he hadn't taken his milk in.'

Maisy shrugged, and then the phone rang over on the desk and she bustled off to answer it in her estate agent persona.

'She's a bit of a fantasist,' Gabriel said, lowering the mug. 'Always prone to making something out of not much, our Maisy.'

I looked over. 'God's gift to estate agency, then.' I sipped. The coffee wasn't bad. 'And thank you for trying to protect me from Harvest Cottage's reputation, but I already know that the previous owner died there.'

'And it doesn't bother you?'

'Any house that's been up for more than fifty years is practically certain to have had someone expire in it, don't you
think? If I ruled out living anywhere with a history of death,
I'd be living on a new estate in Lyme Regis.'

He looked at me steadily. 'This is true. And I don't want
you to get the impression that we're all "oooh, ghosts!" out
here, I just thought it might bother you to be so isolated in a
cottage with that kind of reputation.' He put the mug on the
table and stretched himself out again. 'Think it's a load of old
bollocks myself.'

* * *

I'd been entirely of the 'load of old bollocks' persuasion
myself, but I had to admit the cottage suddenly looked a lot
more spooky when I drove back to it in the rapidly dwindling
daylight. As I swung down the hill I noticed the way you
couldn't see the cottage from the main road, just the oak-lined
lane that trickled down the hill towards it and the steel-grey
line of the river where the ford cut through at the bottom. The
roof didn't become visible until you were practically upon it,
and even then, with all the undergrowth and foliage it was
more of a series of tiled pinnacles, the windows showing dark
and reflectionless, like dead eyes.

'Oh, shut up, Katie,' I chided myself, finding that I was
standing at the front door with my key out, holding my breath
against noises from inside. 'You didn't even think about it
being scary before bloody Maisy and her "weird noises" stuff.'

But I still turned all the lights on as soon as I got inside,
meeting the chill wall of the cold like a solid thing. Lights
helped, as did lighting the range. And the cottage didn't feel
spooky inside, it felt accepting, in a slightly neglected way.

Like a feral cat allowing you to scratch it under the chin, a feeling that it might become so much less strange as it became accustomed to our ways.

I opened the back door and greeted Patrick, who was eating hay from his net, tied safely high in one of the trees. There was something very anti-ghost about the firmly earth-bound Patrick, as though the smell of warm horse and hay drove away anything ethereal more completely than bell, book and candle. You couldn't imagine anywhere in the vicinity of that solid body and squelching feet being haunted; he was simply too *real*. The way he rubbed his head against the tree bark, farted resoundingly and then wandered off to graze was better than an exorcism for driving all spooky thoughts out of my head. I checked his hay, refilled his water bucket and went back in to sit by the warm range with a cup of tea.

I was woken a while later by slamming doors and the return of my daughter.

'Hey, Mum!' And then, suspiciously, 'Were you asleep? Only, like, really *old* people go to sleep in the daytime.' She was wearing a new jacket, one of the fluorescent CREW ones. 'I had a brilliant day! Davin let us walk his dogs all the way to Warram, and I met Rory's mum in the café and they've got all this stuff from the set of that series about the coastguard, and we had custard tarts and then we walked back. Davin is just so *cute* so I've got to tell Shawnia... What's for tea? Dad rang, he's coming over tomorrow to take me out to lunch and I thought I'd get him to take me up to Exeter, Rory says there's some great shops over there, and I need some new clothes.'

I breathed a sigh of relief. If the film crew were coming on Monday to start filming, I could use a Poppy-free day to tidy up and clean a bit before their arrival. 'You don't need new clothes,' I said, almost reflexively. 'You *want* new clothes. It's not the same thing.'

'And they're having a Halloween disco in Steepleton and, like, this kind of fête thing and people dress up and stuff. Rory's asked me to go to the disco with him and it will be a good laugh, everyone goes in costume and they do fortune telling and all that.'

I hadn't missed that she'd dropped the really important part of what she had to tell me in the middle of her speech. You get fluent at teenager speak when you have one; it's just a shame it had taken me so long to get the hang of it. A manual would be useful. Or a translation device.

'So, Rory's asked you to the disco, has he?' I tried to give the words the same lightness as she had. 'He seems nice.'

'He's okay,' and the shrug told me that she'd noticed that I'd noticed. 'His mum's great though, says I might be able to go and work in the café over half-term, and that would be great, cos Dad wants me to go and see Mémé that week and I don't really want to go. Will you tell Dad I've got a job and I can't go?'

She must have got it bad for Rory. Luc's mother was a woman for whom the word 'formidable' had been invented, but she adored her only granddaughter and indulged her to the extent of champagne and grown-up parties. We'd never quite got over the incident of the Coco Chanel dress, Poppy's mémé and I.

'Let's see if the job is a definite first,' I said, trying for maximum diplomacy. 'You wouldn't want to miss a trip over if it's not, would you?'

There was a snort that Patrick couldn't have bettered. 'I might have known you wouldn't want me to do it. I bet you just want me out of the way for that week so you can meet up with your bloke without having me around cramping your style!' The door swung and refused to slam. 'You just don't want me to have any *fun!*' Her feet slammed up the stairs, leaving me perplexed. You'd have thought fourteen years would have made me immune to perplexography, but Poppy seemed to come out with new ways to rock me back on my heels muttering, '*What the hell?*' every day.

Bloke? Did she mean Gabriel? But he wasn't... well, he was male, but that was the only possible way in which he could fit into her created storyline. And if she thought that working in a café was going to be more fun than flying over to France to be alternately babied and fêted by her grand-mére, then I really had absolutely no comeback.

I decided that discretion was the better part of not getting sucked into an argument that wasn't even an argument and I couldn't possibly win. I began dragging together the makings of a meal, and hoped that Gabriel wouldn't keep me hanging on too long for the return of Patrick's hay-net money.

8

I opened the front door on the crisp Monday morning, to a minibus trying to park in the gateway and Keenan squeezing himself out of a 4 x 4 that was only *not* a minibus because of seating numbers.

'Morning, Katie,' he said, artificially brightly, whilst brushing icing sugar off his front. 'We're here to set up for filming, is that all right?'

I stood back to let him in through the front door, whilst a number of people jumped out of the van and began uncoiling wires and lifting boxes of equipment directly over the gate. Patrick clearly thought they'd come to liberate him and went to stand in the way.

'Yes, it's perfect. Got the whole "neglected, yet lived in" vibe.' Keenan came through to the kitchen. 'Peter will be up in the next busload, got to get his shots done before he goes off to the *Broadchurch* docu filming – he's our villain, y'see. We'll do Davin and Larch and the establishing shots later. Nice day for it!'

The low sun was filtering into the kitchen through the

fretwork of leaves that fluttered on the ivy growing up the outside of the cottage. Random shadows came and went like a flickerbook around the walls.

'Yep.' Keenan rubbed his hands together. 'Very serial killer. Almost *too* serial killer, in fact,' and he pulled out a phone. 'Gabe, can you bring us some gear out of props to soften the place up a bit over here? Oh, just like some soft furnishings stuff, couple of easy chairs, rag rug, that kinda thing? If you're not sure, ask Tansy... oh, is she? Okay, well, use your judgement. We just want to make it look more like a home and less like a...' He caught my eye. 'Well, you know. Just some stuff.'

When he hung up, he at least had the manners to look a bit ashamed. 'Sorry. I know it's your home and I didn't mean to impugn your interior design, but we have to use a kind of visual shorthand so the viewer "gets" that this place is a house lived in by someone with serious problems. It's why we asked you not to decorate or do too much to the place.'

Three big men trampled into the kitchen, unspooling wires and hefting plastic boxes full of what seemed to be other plastic boxes. They were all wearing CREW jackets, and I hoped that Poppy hadn't stolen the one currently hanging on the back of her bedroom door. She'd gone off to school very reluctantly, and I had the feeling that it was only the fact that Rory would be at school rather than helping film in the cottage that had got her there.

'It's fine. I'm going to do quite a lot to it when this is all over.' I indicated the men and their boxes. 'I've got plans.'

Keenan adjusted his glasses. 'It's a fabulous little place,' he said, very genuinely. 'I can see what attracted you to it. I'd love a place like this, little getaway in the woods. It's quite fairy-tale, isn't it?'

'Well, it does look as though it was built by someone whose architecture degree came from the Brothers Grimm university,' I said. 'And I suspect that the structural integrity isn't up to much huffing and puffing, but it's fine for us.'

'Yes, I was thinking more on the lines of skipping through woodland glades and breadcrumb trails myself, but I get your point.' He swivelled. 'Starting in the hallway, Neil, so we need the gear through there.' Then back to me. 'It's going to get a bit crowded shortly, Katie. I don't know if you want to hang around or...'

And so I found myself sitting outside my own back door, in the muddy orchard, on the steps to Granny Mary's sausage-scented caravan, with Patrick's head in my lap.

'Very bucolic.' Gabriel wandered out of the kitchen, carrying two mugs of tea. 'Are you all right out here?'

'There isn't room for me in there.' I took the offered mug. 'Last time I stuck my head round the door it was so full of people it was like a clown car, and they were taking the door off the sitting room. I could only observe if I sat up the chimney.'

'Yeah.' He leaned against the steps and Patrick instantly defected to go and snuffle at his pockets. 'Filming isn't the glamorous experience people seem to think. Hence the million-page contract we made you sign. And the *incredibly* ugly chairs you've now got around your kitchen table. Never mind serial-killer cottage, those chairs are an offence against nature in their own right. By the way, I've transferred some money to the account details you gave me.' He slapped lightly at Patrick's shoulder. 'To help cover his expenses.'

'Thank you.' I shivered as a chilly breeze fluttered grey clouds over the sun. The blackbird chinked its alarm call from the hedge like someone hitting a plate with a spoon.

'We can sit in the van,' Gabriel said. 'Mary won't mind. And it's a bit nippy out here.'

'I don't like to,' I said. 'It's a bit like going into someone else's house when they aren't there.'

He stared at me. 'It's *exactly* like going into someone else's house,' he said. 'She lives here.'

'But why?' I followed him up the steps, smelling again that old fried-food smell when he opened the door; it was slightly tempered by the bowl of potpourri on the dresser, but only to the extent that the rose petals made it smell of old-lady fried food. 'Is Granny Mary a born Romani?'

Gabriel scrunched up his face. 'Not really. In fact, not at all, she was born in Solihull and she's spent most of her life as a microbiologist. When she retired, all she wanted to do was travel round Britain, so she bought Patrick and the van and...' he shrugged, '... the rest is a bit of an over-decorated fantasy.'

'Wow.' I looked around again, my view slightly jaded by the knowledge that this wasn't so much culture as cultural appropriation.

'Yes. I think she got most of her ideas from the Famous Five books, but I wouldn't dare say that to Mary. She's happy, and that's what matters.'

I imagined a displeased Granny Mary, and fervently and silently agreed that it was best that she was kept happy.

'And it's not a bad way to live, roaming the countryside.' Gabriel leaned forward to make sure that his mug went down on a coaster on the little shelf beside the built-in settle.

'Until you get ill and have to shove your pony in a stranger's field,' I pointed out.

'Good job she chose a stranger who knows about horses, then.'

I didn't reply. I was looking at the massive amount of decorative work inside the van. The built-in bed at the far end had painted cupboards underneath, there was ornamental tile work around the little stove and enough inlay, filigree and carving work to make a Fabergé manufacturer feel a bit inadequate. 'Overdone' didn't do it justice. 'Even the horse is multicoloured,' I said, a bit weakly.

'And you're a minimalist.' He smiled. 'I like it. The colours are bright enough to register even with my shocking vision, and everything is just where you need it. Okay, it would drive me stir-crazy to have to spend a wet week in here, but it suits Mary.'

There was a weight to the way he said it that made me look at him. 'Yes, and?'

'Nothing.' He was tracing a finger around a carved table edging.

'Gabriel, I live with a teenager. There is not one ounce of nuance that gets past me these days.'

He raised his eyebrows. 'You're good.'

'And?'

'And they want to discharge Mary, but they'll only do it if she's got somewhere stable to live and someone who will keep an eye on her.' He paused. 'Obviously we want her out of the hospital, and I wouldn't expect you to actually have to do anything, Thea and I will pop over and make sure she's all right, but...'

'She needs to stay in the car_____' I said, flatly.

'Well, we *could* move the v_____ but there's nowhere really to park it, and keen_____use the van as well as Patrick – they've got the writer to change the script, with it being a horse, not a pig any more, so...' He tailed off. 'I'm really sorry that you've got tied up in all this,' he finished, somewhat dejectedly. 'It all seemed so simple at first.'

'She hasn't got relatives she could stay with? Friends?'

Gabriel took his glasses off and turned them over in his hands. 'You've met Mary,' he said. 'Does she seem like the sort of woman to have friends? Or friends who could accommodate her for longer than a few days without wanting to bludgeon her to death with a can of soup?'

I looked around at the peaceful orchard. Apart from the occasional banging noise or raised voice from the cottage, and the munching of Patrick, it was very quiet. A late bee bumped against the last apple leaves and hummed off, and the wind whispered through the fallen fruit. If we sat really still, we could hear the gurgle of the ford. Putting Granny Mary into this would be like dropping potassium into a bucket of water.

I hated to admit it, but I'd already got used to Dorset. And I didn't know if I wanted to get used to it with an additional Granny Mary. But then he was right, this van was her home, where else would she go?

'You're thinking about it – that's encouraging.' Gabriel fiddled with the mug handle.

'Well, I can't stop her coming back to her van, can I?'

'I'm sure you could think of a way.'

'But it's her *home*! It's just a bit disconcerting that it's in my field. But she can't stay in hospital forever, and the van is far enough from the house that I won't really need to see her or anything, and she can keep an eye on Patrick.'

Gabriel leaned forward again, but this time it was to look into my face. 'Not so bad at nuance myself, actually,' he said. 'When you can't see so well, you learn to pick up on other stuff and you are absolutely screaming subliminally that you hate the very idea of it, so the fact that your words are saying you'd go for it, well, that means a lot.'

'It's her home,' I said again. 'And, like you said, Keenan wants Patrick and the van out here for – I dunno, it's something to do with the storyline. Quite how we got from pig to horse and caravan, I'm not sure.'

'Serial killers. Bit of a law unto themselves.'

'So, if I want them to carry on filming in my cottage, and I do, because I need the money to get me through the winter, then I need to keep Patrick and the van. Which means, by extension, I get Granny Mary, at least until the filming is all over, which Keenan has absolutely faithfully promised me will be the end of October. Beginning of November at a push. Before Christmas, absolutely definitely.'

'I wouldn't hold him to that,' Gabriel said darkly.

I sighed. Through the little window in the side of the van I could see over the hedge and into the swathe of Dorset that raked off towards the sea. From this height, the sea was just visible as a twinkle beyond the far fields, just a change in the light above the greenery. 'I like it here,' I said, quietly. It was gradually beginning to dawn on me that this was my new life. That Harvest Cottage wasn't just a pause point while I got my breath back and recovered from Luc and London living, but that it might be a place to actually stay. Make a new life.

'It has a few things going for it.' Gabriel picked up his mug again. 'I sometimes have to wrack my brains, but they're there.'

'Views,' I said. 'Light, space.'

'Coastline. We do coastline very well, I've always thought. Bit slumpy, some of it, but that's just a basic design flaw, not really Dorset's fault.'

'I just need to find a job.' I kept my eyes on that distant, flickering horizon. 'If I can find work, then I can put down proper roots, become self-sustaining. I can't rely on film companies making television series on an annual basis.'

'Did you say you used to be a teacher?' He was casually sipping at his tea, lanky body relaxed in his chunky sweater and chinos. Gabriel looked as much part of Dorset as the little brown birds that were cheeping about in the hedge.

'I was a French teacher at a girls' school in London. Bit posh, the sort of place that turns out girls who become ski instructors and chalet girls, all with impeccable language skills, who marry men called Marcel and start their own kitchen-design business.'

We both looked at the cast-iron stove, pretty much the only kitchen that the caravan boasted. 'Yeah, not much call for that round here,' he said.

'I might go into supply teaching. Where they send you into any school that needs you.'

'That sounds stressful.'

'I have to earn money, Gabriel. I've got hardly any savings after buying this place, a teenage daughter who thinks that money comes when you click your fingers and who's used to living in places where there's central heating and a reliable energy supply.' I looked out of the door we'd left open to try to air the smell of frying out of the van, towards the cottage. 'I bought this place on a bit of a whim. Nice long way from London. It's been a bit of a culture shock.'

'So you didn't grow up in a little old cottage and wanted to get back to your roots?' The question was light, as though he was just trying to keep the conversation going, but it made my skin clammy. Had Granny Mary said anything to him? How much did she *really* know about me?

'No. I... we... no. I grew up with more than this.' That was as far as I was going to go. I stood up and picked my mug up from the little table. 'I need to check Patrick's water and hay.'

The whole van moved, a gentle creaking sort of sway, as we both stood up. I put out a hand to steady myself and Gabriel caught at my elbow; we ended up in a kind of close huddle in the middle of the van.

'Sorry.' He let go of my arm. 'Looked as though you were going to fall over.'

'I'm just not used to houses that move. Although Harvest Cottage has its moments when it's windy.'

We looked at one another, slightly embarrassed about the physical contact.

Gabriel and I went slowly down the red and yellow painted steps, where Patrick was standing, droopy lower lipped, in the sloping sunshine. A battalion of wasps bombed fallen apples in the corner of the field, and some blackbirds were arguing over something in the hedge. Through the kitchen window I could see Keenan, a cameraman and a man who must be the elusive Peter, walking round and round the table, on which lay a large machete. Out here it was all peacefully pastoral, in there it looked uncomfortably chaotic, although I was just about certain that Keenan knew what he was doing.

Gabriel followed my look. 'They're going to be at that until they lose the light,' he said gently. 'Kee is a bit of a perfectionist. Do you need to be in there for anything?'

A sudden hopelessness wrapped itself around me like a tight scarf. 'No,' I said, with the realisation dawning that there was absolutely nowhere I needed to be; nothing I needed to be doing. I was completely purposeless, and committed to earning money only through someone else's efforts. Apart from when Poppy had been tiny, I'd worked ever since I graduated, and being at home with a small baby could hardly be described as a holiday. I was now at an end so loose that I was practically unravelling. 'And it feels strange. I was so busy with moving and sorting stuff and settling Poppy into her new school, it's a bit like I've forgotten about myself. That I need things to do.'

'I'm sure something will turn up,' he said gamely. 'Do you knit, at all? Thea's always looking for suppliers for the shop – even she can only produce so many woolly things in a season. And, for some inexplicable reason, holidaymakers like to take home a crocheted memento of their visit more often than you'd think was sane.'

'Nope. Sorry. Absolutely rubbish at handicrafts of all types.'

'Oh.' Gabriel frowned. 'No hobbies you could monetise, then?'

I looked at Patrick, who was resting a plate-like hoof casually, his forelock covering both eyes like a curtain. 'I'm afraid it's teaching or selling my body, and I'm pretty sure that round here teaching will be far more lucrative.'

'I'm sure there are plenty of people who'd pay for your body,' Gabriel said, then *what* he'd said clearly started to filter from his ears back to his brain and a horrified expression dawned. 'Er. That came out very differently from how it was meant to, sorry.'

'I kind of gleaned the meaning without really listening to the words.' I smiled at his confusion. 'It's fine. I appreciate the sentiment. As long as the sentiment is that I'm physically acceptable, rather than that I ought to be making my living on the streets.'

'Wouldn't even need to be the streets these days. Webcam girls are all the rage, so I hear.' Then he dropped his head and took off his glasses. 'Oh, shut up, Gabriel. You're not making things better.' He rubbed a hand across his forehead. 'Should point out that this is purely hearsay and I have no practical experience in these matters. I have to rely on memory these days, I'm afraid.'

The wind swirled the hedge line, twirled about in the tops of the trees and then made its way down to us, tweaking at his hair. It brought home again that he had the dark good looks that should have been escorting actresses into nightclubs and decorating gossip columns. 'I can't believe that girls aren't queueing up for you,' I said, in the 'robust' tone I used to jolly along some of the sad lads who'd trailed in the wake of my students. They'd all been girls with the incredible self-confidence of having parents with enormous wealth, and punctured male egos had surrounded them like deflated netballs.

Gabriel looked up and, for a second, his eyes met mine. There was a dark unreadability in his expression, and almost a look of pain. 'If they are, I can't see them,' he said simply.

'You can see me right now, though, yes?' Feeling a bit embarrassed, although I couldn't tell whether it was from his expression or my words, I waved my hand. 'How many fingers am I holding up?'

He sighed and didn't laugh. 'I can see things that are close to me. Everything else is pretty much a blur and it puts a damper on things pretty fast when it comes to dating.' Another sigh. 'I fall over things a lot too.'

I looked at him sternly. 'But why? Why would nobody want to date you?' And then, adding hastily, 'I am presupposing that there isn't some horrible secret to your existence like you've got previous convictions for something awful?'

He did laugh this time. 'No, nothing terrible. Just that Dorset is the last resting place of womenkind who like their men of the macho persuasion. Either farmers' daughters who can throw round bale silage over their heads and want a man who can outdo them at weightlifting, or those who've bought themselves a nice little weekend retreat and want copious amounts of fiscal input. I don't really rate on either of those scales. I'm so beta I should come with a test warning.'

'Plenty of women like that, though.' I leaned against Patrick, who opened an eye, then closed it again, changed resting hooves and drooped his head lower. 'I mean, you've *seen* Tom Hiddleston, right? Beating them off with a stick, and he's not exactly Dwayne Johnson.'

Gabriel flashed me a grin. 'Well, thanks for the comparison. But I have it on good authority, and by that I mean Keenan, that Mr Hiddleston isn't a visually impaired Dorset lad.' He came over and fussed with Patrick's mane. 'Kee met him doing some perfume ad or something. He was impressed, but then Keenan is quite easy to impress if you wear designer gear. Sorry, am I self-pitying again?'

'A bit.'

I wondered. With some well-placed flirting Gabriel could find himself a woman who didn't really care about his gruesome eyesight and lack of chest-beating. His lanky build and well-shaped face would be a great addition to pretty much anyone's life. Plus, he seemed like a nice guy. So, what was it *really* keeping everyone away?

'I was bullied.' He carried on fussing with Patrick, and the words so neatly answered my question that I thought for a moment I'd spoken them aloud. 'Through school. My eye condition was diagnosed when I was nine, and I've worn glasses that get thicker every year ever since. Twenty-three years of squinting at life through jam jars, and having that fact remarked on by everyone I was at school with, often with a little added dig about my inability to perform normal manly tasks. It kind of marks you.'

I remembered the way he'd hunched his way past the darts players in the pub, trying to keep out of the line of sight, stay invisible. 'Oh, Gabriel,' I said. 'No wonder you—'

'I used to love swimming,' he carried on with a determined set to his jaw, as though I had to hear it all. 'I was on the school team. I was good. But the rest of the guys used to hide my clothes, drop my stuff in the pool. They beat me up one evening after practice and broke my glasses. I stopped going.'

I felt my inner teacher twitch. 'That was completely wrong, and completely on them,' I said. 'I hope you haven't been carrying around some kind of misplaced guilt because a bunch of inadequates needed to make you feel inferior.'

I must have sounded fierce, because Patrick snapped his head up and tossed his mane back, drawing all four feet underneath him as though prepared to leap sideways. Gabriel jumped back. 'Hey, horse, calm down.'

'And *that* sort of behaviour is why Patrick needs to go somewhere else. I don't want Poppy sitting on him again. Anything could happen.'

'I don't think Granny Mary would stand for Patrick having temperament.' Gabriel shivered. 'Any kind of flightiness and she'll have him up the glue factory.'

'They're unreliable,' I said, and I could hear how tight my voice sounded. 'Any horse can do anything. Even Patrick.'

Raised voices from the cottage broke my train of thought, and both of us looked over towards the kitchen, from where indoor lights that the film crew had brought were spilling out over the muddy grass. In my pocket, my phone buzzed a text incoming.

From: Pop Pops

Hey mum, is it okay if I get the bus back with Rory to Warram and you can pick me up later, say about six?

It was already four o'clock, which accounted for the low sun and the increasing chill of the breeze. 'Sorry, it's Poppy,' I said. 'She wants me to pick her up from Rory's later.'

I texted back, telling her it was probably just as well as they were filming in the cottage, and got back a single grinning emoticon.

'Would you like a lift back to Steepleton, or are you waiting for the crew bus?' I said. 'I might drive over to Warram a bit early, get to meet Rory's mum if she's there, take a look at the café where Poppy wants to work. It's better than standing around out here listening to them filming *The Shining* Part Two.'

He shook his head. He seemed a little bit embarrassed, as though he felt telling me about the bullying had reduced him in my eyes. I'd seen it in children before, a reluctance to admit that they weren't coping with something, as though they thought that they had to appear to be supreme beings at all times. As though vulnerability was something shameful. 'I'd better wait for Kee. He might want me to scope something out, if he finds today hasn't worked.'

'Oh. Okay.'

We began a joint trudge along the path that Patrick had beaten down to the back door. Gabriel was keeping his head down, ostensibly watching his feet in their practical boots, but I thought he was probably trying to avoid my eye. Just as we got to the door, he put out a hand and stopped me.

'Katie – I, uh, I'd be grateful if you didn't mention anything I've said here.'

I looked at him aghast. 'Who to? I'm not exactly going to stick posters up, am I?'

A quick smile flashed over his face. 'No. But, if you meet my sister. Thea doesn't know how bad school was for me. I left without much in the way of qualifications. My family put it all down to my sight failing and I never told them it was mostly because I spent a lot of time bunking off and hiding in the woods.'

'Gabriel, you were *bullied*. It wasn't your fault.'

For a second I got a quick glimpse of the scared little boy he must have been. Just because now he was a dramatically good-looking six feet of humanity clearly didn't mean that a traumatised eleven-year-old wasn't still peering out from inside.

'I know. I really do. But they already worry enough about me. I don't want to give them retrospective worry, if you see what I mean. And they might – well, they might say I should have told them then. And yes, I should have, and yes, it could all have been different if I hadn't kept quiet, kept the secret, tried to manage it myself but... well.' He pushed a hand through his hair. 'So, just between me and you, is that okay?'

It had cost him to tell me. I could see from the way new lines had etched around his eyes and his mouth. I channelled all my teacher training, all those long hours of child protec-tion. It had been twenty years ago, more, that all this had started; there was nothing I could do for him but listen and believe. 'I won't say anything. But you—'

'I should tell them, I know. But, not yet, all right?'

He reached out a hand. I thought he was going to push the

door open, but it just stayed there, wobbling about between me and the door.

'I'm waiting for a handshake,' he said, after a moment.

'Are you? Oh.' I took the hand and shook it, feeling again the way his long fingers wrapped around mine. His skin was warm, but so was mine, as the flush dropped down my head and encompassed most of my body in a tight sweater hug of embarrassed misunderstanding.

Just then Keenan flung open the door and stared at both of us as though he'd forgotten we existed. 'I was just going to have a dramatic strop around the field, but you've somewhat discombobulated me now.'

'I do my best.' Gabriel stepped past him. 'Now, it sounds as though there might be tension I must defuse. Lead me to your path of least resistance.'

I picked up my car keys and left them all to it.

* * *

When I walked into the café at Warram Bay, I was surprised to see how busy it was. Rory and Poppy were sitting at a corner table talking quietly, and we all pretended not to see each other.

'You Poppy's mum, then?' the lady behind the counter asked as she took my order for coffee and a slice of cake. 'You looks a lot alike. I'm Karen, Rory's mum.' Then she lowered her voice under the sound of jetting steam. 'We'd better pretend that we don't know them. It looks serious over there.'

She jerked her head towards the corner. Rory was drawing something on a pad and Poppy was watching intently. I felt a sudden pang for the little girl who'd once watched me with such rapt attention. Sometimes the gulf between who she'd been and who she was now was filled with such sad moments.

'Poppy was saying that you might have a job for her over here?' I looked around. The café walls were lined with memorabilia from a TV series that I'd only caught occasionally, framed scripts and costumes and large colour photographs of a cast standing laughing on clifftops. Almost all the tables were full and a small bouncy dog that looked as if a racehorse had somehow inexplicably mated with a dreadful wig was snuffling around legs.

'It's a community-owned café – Tansy does our books and sorts us out, but I'm the one here most, so I gets final say. If she wants it, job's there,' Karen said. 'We gets really busy in the holidays too, and since Mags moved over to Lyme to look after the grandbabies, there's not really enough of us. Rory was going to help out, but Neil's got him working as part of the sound crew over to Steepleton, so he's a fat lot of use. Mind you, he'd be a fat lot of use in here anyway, you know what lads is like.'

I didn't really, but Karen's absolute certainty that I'd know what she was talking about and who the mysterious 'Mags' might be didn't look as though it would take denial well.

'It would be good for her to get some work experience.' I held out a fiver, but Karen waved it away.

'These all pays a good markup, means we can slip the odd bun under the counter, if you see what I mean.' She nodded at the crowded café. 'Mind you, Zummat does a good job of clearing up any leftovers.' She eyeballed the dog sternly. 'Rory! You make sure you takes Zummat out before you starts your homework. He's just eaten a full muffin and I don't want *that* coming back at three o'clock on the landing, thank you very much.'

'His name's Summer, Mum,' Rory said, slightly plaintively. 'After the direwolf in *Game of Thrones*.'

Karen raised an eyebrow. 'That dog's no closer to a dire-wolf than I am,' she said. 'His dad's called Brian and his mum's Davin's whippet. He's zummat or nothin', that dog, and he always will be. You sit down with your coffee, love, and I'll come over for a chat. We're near to closing here, so it'll get quieter now.'

I sat and drank my coffee and ate the very squishy cake. Summer (or whatever the dog's name was) came and made pathetic noises near my ankles until Karen came back, when he moved off to hoover crumbs from another table.

'Hear they're using your cottage up over the hill there,' Karen said, pulling out a chair. 'Filming going all right? Young Gabriel was over here t'other day. They're doing some scenes up on the beach there. Serial killer, so I heard.'

I nodded. I hadn't quite got used to the way news travelled around here, in a kind of daisy-chain way. Everyone seemed to know everyone else, and be connected in various esoteric ways; if you lost your phone over in Steepleton, someone in Dorchester would ask if you'd checked the pocket of your black jacket.

'It's been a bit of an eye-opener,' I said. 'At first I'd thought they'd just use the cottage for a day and be gone, but Keenan seems to think they're going to be there for ages.'

Karen shooed the dog away again. 'One thing I've learned from this TV lot,' she said, putting her feet up on the chair next to her, 'they don't hurry. Mind you, Davin is a perfec-tionist and I'm not sure Larch *can* hurry. She's only got one speed, that girl, and it's "waft".'

I looked over to where Poppy was correcting something Rory had drawn, talking earnestly. Away from her usual habitat she looked older, and I realised that I rarely saw her like this. Usually we were together, mother and daughter, and she was being 'daughter' as hard as she could. Here she was an autonomous being, and I felt a tiny shiver in my chest. Another four years and she'd be an adult, grown and gone.

Karen had obviously seen my look. She leaned forward over the table, her arms spread across the slightly sticky surface. 'They'll be fine. You've no need to worry,' she said, in a low voice. 'My Rory knows what's what and he's keen to get good exam results and go up to college. He won't go messing her about.'

I realised what she was *really* saying, and felt a momentary flood of relief. I'd had The Talk with Poppy, met with a curled lip and a dismissive eye-roll, but it was nice to know that Rory's mum seemingly had had a similar talk. Poppy was assertive and not one to be easily persuaded into a situation she might have trouble getting out of, but fourteen-year-old girls can get put in some tricky positions, some of them not entirely unwanted, and I was glad that Karen wasn't any keener to be a precipitous grandmother than I was.

'And you've got Granny Mary's van in your orchard too,' Karen carried on, a little louder now, presumably so that Rory and Poppy didn't suspect we'd been talking about them. She could have saved the effort; Poppy *always* assumed I was talking about her behind her back. 'Gabriel was saying that they're going to let her out, long as she can go back to the van. You'll have your work cut out with that one. Have you met Granny Mary?'

I explained that Gabriel and I had been over to the hospital a couple of days ago, whilst trying to be circumspect about my reaction to Granny Mary. For all I knew Karen was a close relative – from her expression, one of the ones who'd beat Mary to death with a soup can after a week. 'She's a... very unconventional lady,' I said, carefully.

'Ah. Gabe's a saint, that boy. Known him and his sister since I moved here from Lyme, just before Rory was born. He was a strange one back then, but he's filled out nice enough.' Karen looked at me thoughtfully. 'Shame about the whole...' She made circles around her eyes with a forefinger. 'He'd be a right stunner otherwise.'

I was so glad someone else could see that I was a little over-effusive. 'Yes, he's really nice. He actually seems to like Granny Mary, and he's said he and his sister will keep an eye on her when she has to move back. I've got my hands pretty full with them filming at the cottage and... stuff...' I tailed off, realising that it sounded like the biggest excuse ever not to get involved with a poorly elderly lady. 'And they want her van and Patrick to be part of the storyline, so we can't move them. Apparently,' I added.

'Mmm. Went out with Gabe, once or twice, when Rory was a tiny lad.' Karen looked down at the tabletop, and picked a loose bit of varnish off with a fingernail. 'He's a year or so younger than me, mind, but there's not much of a dating pool round here. More of a puddle! We've all mostly been round the block with each other – anyone within five years is fair game.'

I tried to imagine Gabriel dating Karen and my brain made odd noises. Slightly shy, slightly awkward Gabriel and this very confident, together lady? Nope, I just couldn't see it, even fifteen years ago.

Karen shook her head and stopped picking. 'Wouldn't have worked,' she said. 'Even if he hadn't nearly drowned me. He's not really my type – I just got a bit hormonal. And he's pretty gorgeous.'

'He nearly drowned you?'

'It was an accident.'

Poppy came over, Rory at her elbow. 'We've worked out our costumes for the Halloween party,' she said happily. 'I'm going to be Cersei and Rory's going to be Jaime. It's going to be *amazing*!'

'I thought you were doing homework,' I said, slightly weakly.

'Mum! Dur! I'll do my homework when I'm at *home* – the clue is in the name! This was more important! Rory says that he'll talk to Sharon who does costume for *Spindrift* and she might help us sort costumes.'

Rory nodded furiously and silently.

'You're not to bother the crew,' Karen said mildly. 'They've got a show to make, not worry about kitting you two up out of *Doctor Who*.'

'Mum!' Rory looked genuinely shocked. 'It's *Game of Thrones*! We could get Summer to be our direwolf.'

We all looked over to where Summer was scratching behind an ear, with half a discarded baguette sticking out of the side of his mouth, like a nonchalant cigarette.

'Or maybe not,' Rory finished, pragmatically. 'He might get in the way a bit, up the disco.'

'Right, now you two toddle off home. Rore, you can give me a hand wiping down in here, now we're closed.' Karen swung her legs down off the seat and stood up. 'Poppy, you're welcome to come and earn a few bob here at the weekends and in the holiday, but I don't want you compromising your education during the week.' She gave me a sideways nod and a wink. 'Work hard at school and we'll pay you over the minimum for when you're in here. If your mum says your marks are slipping or you're not doing your homework, then you'll have to give up in here.'

Poppy beamed her a smile. 'I will, thanks, Karen!'

I was impressed. Admittedly Karen was a couple of years ahead of me in the 'owning a teenager' stakes, but she'd clearly got a firm handle on management.

Poppy and I drove back in the gathering darkness. She was concentrating on her phone screen, occasionally letting out little whoops, or taking pictures of herself to send to friends, although, since all her friends knew what she looked like and the backdrop was merely the dark inside of my car, I didn't know why. When I'd been young it had been hours and hours spent on the house phone, although, now I came to think of it, I'd never really done it like my friends. Things had been different for me.

The cottage was dark and silent when we got back. The keys had been left under the approved brick and every trace of the film crew was gone, apart from the fact that the bushes around the front door were more beaten back and the mossy path around the side of the cottage had been trodden to a black slime. Inside it was almost clinically tidy, although the table was still off-centre and the mismatched chairs that Keenan insisted were more 'serial killer' were still in evidence, while my rather nicer ones were stacked in the hall. I assumed this meant the crew would be back tomorrow.

'Night, then, Mum,' Poppy trilled chirpily, flinging herself out of the car. 'I'll go and do homework now.'

'But – food?'

'Ate at the café.' And then, because we'd had lots of talks about eating and control and she'd had a friend whose anorexia had torn her family apart, 'Honest, Mum, you can ask Karen. She does these really great paninis.' And, as she skipped off upstairs, no doubt to message everyone she knew on WhatsApp, with a desultory attempt at homework, I felt that squeeze of panic that was probably common to anyone bringing up teenagers in the minefield of modern-day life.

So much to worry about. Were they meeting unsuitable people online, or eating the wrong thing or being forced into sex or blackmailed into sending naked pictures? I tried to keep communication lines open with Poppy, but she had the secretive nature of the typical teen and sometimes I was filled with horror at what might happen. Or even was happening, and I couldn't see it.

I had to pour myself a glass of water and sit down. My stomach didn't like this line of thinking and I usually tried to distract myself away from it. But here in the kitchen, with the single bulb barely illuminating a central circle, and the corners all shadowy little hiding spaces, there wasn't much distraction. Deep breaths. Don't let the thoughts in. Don't let imagination run away with...

... What was that noise? Outside, where it was fully dark now, there was a strange sound. A tapping, but too irregular to be a branch in the wind and, besides, a quick glance at the silhouetted bushes showed not a breath of breeze. Yet still *rattletap* pause. *Rattletaptap.*

I tiptoed to the back door and tried to look out but the Dorset darkness was total. No distant pinpricks of light as the hill stopped any of the light from Steepleton from showing and no other lights travelled as far as this little valley. There was, however, a strong smell of warm horse. 'Patrick?' I whispered, and turned on the torch on my phone.

Patrick was standing with his back to the door, half a tree branch tangled in his tail and swishing against the wood with every half-hearted sweep. He heard me, and stumped around to push his nose into my pocket, his big head heavy but reassuring against me. 'Sorry. I almost forgot you were out here. Let's do your hay and water.'

Well, there was no one else to talk to. Poppy was a series of thumps and the odd burst of music when her headphones fell out. The crew had gone. The woodlice weren't great conversationalists, so it was either talk to Patrick or start the sort of mumbling monologue that would make Poppy roll her eyes and talk about putting me in a home. Not for the first time, the sheer loneliness of my new life at Harvest Cottage hit me. I'd been busying myself so much lately that it had kept the feelings at bay, but now it was back, the realisation that I'd gone from central London and a life with pupils and friends and the floating presence that Luc had become once we'd split up, to this. No houses within my sightline. Friends who were at the end of a phone, but distracted now by a life I wasn't part of any more. And a darkness that was so thick I could practically cut pieces out of it as I stepped outside with the bucket slopping cold water on my feet.

Patrick's hay net was still full, so I topped up his water, gave him a pat, and left him for the night, grazing contentedly on the slope that his hooves hadn't turned into mud. There was something so solid and reassuring about the smell and sound of him that I almost relaxed. But only almost, in the same way as I could *almost* hear the squeaky chirrups of woodlice egging one another on to slide down the wall, or *almost* imagine that Gabriel had looked at me with more than the amusement of a local for a displaced Londoner.

I followed Poppy's example, and went to bed.

9

The days began to fall into a pattern, although it was a pattern so complicated that William Morris would have pronounced that it gave him a headache.

My alarm woke Poppy and I in time for her to drag herself ready for school. Once she was on the bus, I would open the doors and air the cottage, feed Patrick, and await the film crew. Sometimes I'd get a text from Keenan or Gabriel saying that they were going to film elsewhere while the conditions were right, on which occasions I'd spend the day doing laundry or scanning the job adverts or tweaking my CV and sending it to local teaching agencies. I also developed a worrying tendency to bake, mostly because it warmed up the kitchen and made the place smell less like a deserted shed in some woods somewhere.

On other days the crew would turn up at nine, and I'd watch the filming, which brought me into contact with both Davin and Larch, the leading couple. Both gorgeous, both incredibly argumentative, although mostly only with each other, and both prone to being rather 'starry', although Davin was a lot better when Tansy came with him, and he made a great cup of tea. Larch could be sweetly childlike sometimes, and I'd taught her how to sew buttons on, a skill she'd acquired with the same delight as I imagined someone learning to do advanced algebra.

Gabriel and I slid past one another. He was busy scoping out some sites for filming inland, near Beaminster, so I didn't see much of him until the Saturday morning. Poppy had stayed overnight at Karen's to work a trial shift in the café ('It's fine, Mum, Rory's going to sleep on the sofa and I can have his room,' almost as though she didn't believe I'd ever been fourteen or known any sixteen-year-old boys), so I'd woken up late to a tap on the front door, and Patrick neighing.

The weather was the kind of grey misty fog that seemed to drift in from the sea increasingly often now we were well into autumn. It was like having net curtains up at all the windows, and the lack of light had pushed me to oversleep quite dramatically.

'Hello?' I poked my head around the door, chastity-dressing gown clasped around my body.

'Er, hi.' It was Gabriel. 'Sorry, am I disturbing you?'

I opened the door to let him in. 'From doing what? I've got no job and the highlight of my days is watching Larch and Davin argue.'

'Well, you were...' He waved a hand to take in my pyjama'd form. 'You might have been entertaining guests.'

I led the way through to the kitchen, which, on this damp and grey morning, was practically underwater. The table shone with a film of damp and the kettle had beads of condensation forming along it. 'Entertaining? I'm not exactly dressed to do a song and dance act, am I?'

He blinked at me. 'I meant... you know. In bed.'

The penny dropped and I had to turn away to fill the kettle to cover my suddenly hot cheeks. 'Oh. No. No entertaining of that nature goes on in here. Of any nature really, although I did rewatch series one of *Stranger Things* yesterday.' I let the tap run longer than I should have and water spurted out of the kettle.

'Oh. Good.' Behind me I heard Gabriel pull out a chair, feel the slightly slimy dampness of the wood and decide to leave sitting down for another room. Or house.

'"Good"? You don't *want* me to have any entertainment?'

'I just meant that this would be harder if there was, you know—' a glance upwards at the ceiling '—someone else here.'

He blinked at me again. The mist was gradually falling from his hair and coat, where it had formed exotic shimmering beads. It melted into water, which made his hair darker. His eyes were very big behind his glasses. I wondered what he was going to do that would be difficult if someone else were there, and was torn between readying myself for a kiss and clutching for the handle of the kitchen knife.

'Why are you leaning? Are you all right?'

His tone of concern pulled me back to the reality of a full kettle and Gabriel's hand on my shoulder, pushing me slightly. My face went hot again as I realised I'd unconsciously moved forward for a kiss that, most evidently, was not on the cards.

'Floor is a bit uneven.' I went back to plug in the kettle. 'Tea?'

'They're bringing Granny Mary home today.'

The words fell like a concrete lump into the damp atmosphere. 'Oh.' I fetched the teabags, feeling the strange stirring of an almost-resentment in my chest. Was I resenting

Granny Mary coming back to her van? Disturbing my de facto ruling of Harvest Cottage? Or the fact that Gabriel hadn't even *considered* kissing me?

'She honestly won't disturb you at all.' Gabriel perched himself on the edge of the table. I put down the fact that I noticed how long his legs were to a nasty attack of hormones, and dropped an extra teabag into my mug. 'She's only staying until the doctors have given her the okay to move on. Won't be more than a couple of weeks. Or so,' he added. 'She'll just be in the van, maybe ask for some water now and again to refill the tank.'

I tried again to prevent myself from wondering about the toilet arrangements. 'Patrick will be pleased to see her.'

'Patrick is pleased to see anyone who brings food.' Gabriel was watching me and it was disconcerting.

'So, when is she arriving?' The kettle began to hum a boil and I busied myself with it and fetching the milk from the fridge.

'In about an hour.'

'What, *today*?' I rounded on him in alarm. 'But... I need to go and air the van! And maybe give Patrick a bit of a brush down, or at least disentangle the worst of the landscape from his tail.'

'Well, we could open up the van now,' he suggested. 'After you've... I mean, it's quite chilly out there and you...' A hand waved, taking in my dressing gown. 'It *is* your pyjamas, isn't it? It's not some kind of new fashion?'

I glared. 'Okay, I know your eyesight is failing, but surely you can tell the difference between nightwear and current fashion?'

He got up off the table edge and came over. 'It's hard to tell. You've not met my sister, have you? She wears stuff that could be fashion, could be tablecloth and I daren't ask. She gave me lychees once, told me they were eyeballs when I was halfway through eating them and I don't think Mum ever quite forgave either of us. Siblings, it's a double-edged sword.'

'I wouldn't know,' I said, a bit stiffly. 'I'm an only child.'

'And your daughter is an only child too?' He took the mug of tea from me. The steam instantly condensed on his glasses.

'Why do you make it a question? Do you suspect me of having half a dozen children tucked away somewhere?' I didn't know why his questions were making me so uneasy. Well, yes, I did, any questions about my background made me uneasy, even if they were innocently asked.

Gabriel took off the steamy glasses and laid them on the worktop. 'You could have older children,' he said, reasonably. 'Away at university or something.'

'I'm *thirty-four*! I had Poppy when I was twenty! Any older children I would have to have had while I was at school,' I said, with an unmistakable note of indignation rising with the steam from my mug.

'I didn't know you were thirty-four.' That reasonable tone was beginning to get annoying now.

'Well, I am.'

The silence was only broken by the sound of two people trying to drink very hot tea as quickly as possible. I began to wonder how the hell people ever managed to make conversation, seeing as Gabriel and I seemed to plunge ourselves so deeply into the pool of embarrassment and misunderstanding that we practically drowned in discomfiture.

'Well,' I said, putting down my half-empty cup. 'I'll just dash out and open up the van, get some air into it.'

'And I'll... well, I'll just generally mill around, shall I?' He picked up his glasses. 'And try not to make any more faux pas.'

I handed him the dandy brush I'd bought when I'd got the hay net. 'You could give Patrick a bit of a tidy up if you like.'

Gabriel stared at the brush. 'I'm not really very horsey.'

'Brush. You know, brush brush. Like hair, only bigger. And more equine.'

A sudden smile illuminated his face. It crinkled his eyes, made him look mischievous and horribly sexy, with that soft fall of dark hair and those cheekbones that went on forever. 'I might be able to get the hang of that. As long as he stands still.'

Ignoring the smile, I threw open the back door and let the welcome coolness of the foggy morning in. He needn't think he could smile like that and have me – well, whatever effect he thought it would have. I was impervious to charm. I'd been married to a *Frenchman*, for God's sake, and look how that had turned out.

Inside the van felt a good deal drier than the house. I opened the little side window and the door to let a through draught in, although the air outside was very still, weighted down by all the water. A faint and reluctant sun was oozing through the mist in a jagged and patchy way but having no effect on heating up the air – in fact, all it was doing was releasing that 'autumnal' scent, which smelt as if someone had set fire to blackberries.

Outside I could hear Gabriel talking soothingly to Patrick, who was pulling chunks from his hay net, and the rasping sound of a dandy brush on patches of mud. There was a peculiar feeling somewhere between my ribs and stomach, and I had to sit on the little bench seating opposite the tiny stove for a moment as it gripped me; it felt as though someone had torn a hole through my skin and was allowing the day into my heart.

I felt *happy*. I wasn't a complete stranger to happiness, of course not, there were moments of happiness in every day – Poppy giving me a sudden hug, the smell of new baking coming out of the oven, a really good cup of tea first thing in the morning, surrounded by birdsong. But this happiness was different. More of a low simmering kind of enjoyment of everything around me. The smell of polish and frying inside the van, the chill of outside with its top note of mud, stomped grass and old vegetation. The sound of Gabriel's voice murmuring and Patrick's occasional squelch. The rock of dissatisfaction that usually weighted down my stomach dissolved in the quotidian. Odd.

'Are you all right in there?' Gabriel appeared in the little doorway, hair awry and a mud-clotted brush in his hand. 'You've gone very quiet.'

Behind him, Patrick snorted hay dust.

'I'm just feeling...' I took a deep breath. The smell of old fat was definitely less now; I must have been sitting for a while. 'Happy. I'm realising that moving to Dorset probably wasn't such a stupid idea.'

He came a little further into the van, shoving the brush into his pocket. 'Why did you think it was before? It's an odd kind of revelation to have on a damp morning. It's a lot nicer round here when the sun is out.'

'Did you ever leave?' I didn't really look at him as I asked, and instead kept my eyes on the brightly painted cupboard by the stove.

'I was in Exeter for a while. And I live in Bridport now. It's not exactly *Bright Lights, Big City*, but I have travelled. This isn't all I know.' His voice was quiet. There was something of the same tone as I'd heard him using to Patrick, something gentle. 'I had to get away for a while, so I went round Europe with nothing but a backpack and an inept understanding of how to say "more beer, please" in five European languages.'

'Did you enjoy it?'

'Well, I got drunk a lot.' He came further inside. 'And saw lots of landmarks. Well, bits of them.' The glasses came off again and he turned them around in his hands. 'It was a bit crazy, to tell the truth, but then, everyone goes a bit off the rails when they're young, don't they?'

'Don't say that, Poppy's fourteen. I'm expecting an "off the rails" moment any day now.'

'Is that why you're snatching this moment of feeling happy? You're expecting the wheels to come off any second?'

It was a considered question, as though he'd thought about it rather than was just making conversation. I took a breath to answer, then realised I didn't know what the answer really was. *Was* I waiting for it all to go wrong?

'I only ask because you've got this kind of...' He waved his hands, sketching the air around me.

'Dressing gown?' I tried to guess. 'Bad haircut? Smell?'

'Aura. Only it's not an aura, that's not my thing – if you want auras read then you have to ask Thea, she's got friends who go in for that sort of thing, all candles and chanting and doing one another's cards. I just mean...' He dropped his hands and his glasses clattered against the dandy brush in his pocket. 'You have this kind of thing like you need to hold everything close to you to keep it safe. And anything outside that little circle is a bit... dangerous? Am I making sense?'

'Not really,' I said, a bit stiffly.

'It's just that I see more than a lot of people.' Gabriel went on, clearly taking no notice of my shivery discomfort. 'I mean, not literally, but because I can't see very well I tend to look more. Does that make sense? I dunno, maybe the bullying did me a favour in that way. I like to work people out, find out what their motives are before I get too close – saves me from getting my glasses nicked and stamped on too often.' His tone was light, although the words were so horribly serious. 'So, I wait. I watch. Blurrily, usually. It gives me an idea of how people are feeling. And then, if they're feeling punchy, I can get out, because it's not much fun always being the target.' Tone still light, almost as though it were a big joke being picked on and beaten up.

I felt that twist of awkwardness in my chest. He was telling me so much about himself, trying to get me to open up and yet I just couldn't. 'Maybe I'm just starting to settle in to Harvest Cottage properly,' I said, with a brightness so breezy that it almost flapped the curtains.

He took a step back. Put his glasses back on, turning away. 'Yes. Maybe.' The light tone was gone now, his voice was flat.

I wanted to say something. To tell him that I wasn't knocking him back with his confidences and his confessions, but I just *couldn't* – and then Patrick let out a squeal that made both of us jump towards the door. It was the high-pitched squeal of a horse who's injured or trapped or just…

'How's my bonny boy, then?'

Granny Mary came up the steps into the van and caught us both in attitudes of arrested horror.

'You're…' I started.

'We heard Patrick,' Gabriel said, no more fluently than me.

Granny Mary, looking a little bent, but about as frail as a Ford Transit, raised her eyebrows. I saw her take in my pyjamas under the double wrapping of my dressing gown and then rake on to find the large bulge in Gabriel's coat, which I knew was the dandy brush but very much suspected that she thought was something else.

'Well, I'm clearly interrupting something,' she said. 'But as this is my house, you'll have to go and do it somewhere different. Any chance of a brew?'

Gabriel and I looked at one another.

'And it's me that's had the stroke, so you needn't look so wooden, the pair of you. Katie, your cottage seems to be full of men and they're all sitting round the table, so now might be the time to go and get that tea made.'

Granny Mary bustled past us and began fiddling with things inside the van, opening cupboards and sniffing as though she thought we'd been about to steal her best china. Gabriel jerked his head towards the door, I nodded and we tried to slide out unobtrusively, past Patrick, who was beside himself with happiness and trying to climb the steps.

'She seems well,' Gabriel said, and it was his turn to sound more artificially bright than the stage lights that were currently illuminating my kitchen.

'If by "well" you mean "horrible", then yes,' I half whispered.

'She's lovely really.' He'd lowered his tone to match mine. 'Just a bit... brusque.'

'*Brusque!* She makes Severus Snape sound like the Queen.' I was practically hissing now. 'And she's living in *my orchard*?'

Any reply that Gabriel might have been about to make was cut off by Keenan, who threw open the kitchen door and stood, backlit by the ferocious set lights. 'Is that the van owner turned up? Oh, good, now we can get permission to use it and the horse. I'll go and talk to her.'

'I'd give her a minute,' Gabriel said. 'She's only just arrived.'

'I'd give her about forty years,' I said, snidely. 'And even then I wouldn't expect her to be polite.'

'Oh dear.' Keenan stepped back into the kitchen. 'Well, I'm sure I can work my charm on her, but you're right, we'll let her settle in first.'

'She wants a cup of tea.' I went and shook the kettle, more of a reflex action than anything else because at least four men were sitting around the table with steaming mugs in front of them. 'Maybe you could take it to her? Break the ice that way?'

'Good idea.' Keenan began making more tea, while everyone around the table stared at Gabriel and I as though we were interrupting something.

'I'm going to get dressed.' I adjusted the dressing gown, grateful for my sturdy 'bloody cold bedroom' pyjamas. 'And then I'm going to leave you to it.'

They continued to stare.

'Gabriel, you can liaise with your lady about the van and horse,' Keenan said, shaking biscuits onto a plate. 'Introduce me, give me a hand with the practicalities.'

Gabriel looked as though he was about to object for a moment, threw a quick glance at me, and then looked at his feet. 'Of course,' he said, and then his eyes came back up to me again and I saw a look that held a little betrayal in it and I wasn't sure why. 'And then I'll head back to Steepleton, if that's okay, Kee.'

'If you want a lift, I'll be going down that way,' I found myself saying, although I'd actually been planning a drive to Dorchester, to the supermarket. 'I need to pick up a few bits in the shop.'

Gabriel gave me a long, steady look. 'No, thank you,' he said. 'I'll be fine.'

I'd hurt him, that much was clear. But I wasn't really quite sure how.

* * *

Christmas Steepleton was quiet when I arrived. There were the usual crew lorries and vans around the little harbour, but they'd finished filming on the beach, so the equipment wasn't in evidence.

I parked at the end of the road, in the little car park that overlooked the sea, and took some deep breaths. To my left, the shops ran along the road that hung above the beach, restrained only by some railings from actually falling onto the beach huts below. To my right, the harbour was full of fishing boats, twisting and clanging at anchor on a high tide, some vicious-looking seagulls bobbing alongside them in the chilly water. The coast stretched away to either side, nibbled to bays and cliffs by the waves, which clonked and hushed benignly in the still air, looking incapable of the resculpting of the geography they clearly carried out in worse weather.

There was nobody about. Unsurprising really, as the day was still full of shifting grey air. Not the thick mist that had enveloped the morning, but a dusting of water that blocked most of the further view beyond the cliff edges and made sure any surfaces were dotted with condensation, although not quite enough to stop my windscreen wipers from squeaking like tortured stoats against the glass.

I got out of the car and was almost instantly soaked. Umbrellas would be useless against this damp, which came at you sideways like sea ghosts, so I hunched my shoulders in my town-adequate jacket, pulled my hood around my ears, and walked up towards the inviting lights of the shops with my hands deep in my pockets.

I hadn't *needed* to go to Dorchester. The larder was still full from the online shop I'd had delivered a few days ago – although I wouldn't have put it past the crew to have had a party and eaten all the crisps, and Keenan to have discovered my eighty-five per cent chocolate, even though I'd hidden it behind the dusters. If anyone ever found the half bottle of vodka that I kept for extreme emergencies, life would become impossible.

I just wanted some fresh fruit, possibly some vegetables, although Poppy seemed to regard anything less fancy than pak choi to be inedible. If I chopped them up small and put them in the slow cooker she could sometimes be persuaded to eat carrots and celery, but only if they were fresh. So here I was in Steepleton, where the only shop to sell food that wasn't ice cream or iced buns appeared to double as the post office, off-licence and fishing-bait shop. I wandered around in there for a while; they didn't have any vegetables that looked any newer than my delivery, so I bought some stamps because I felt guilty, and a couple of postcards to send to my mother. She'd still be in Australia, I expected, but it showed willing if I sent her something from our new home.

I chose cards that showed the whole bay, wide and blue under a summer sun. Found a pen in my pocket and scribbled a neutral message, then put the card in the postbox. Duty done. Then I walked the length of the promenade, to where the shops petered out into a small shack with a sign 'P Smith, Woodcarver' over the locked door, and a path that ran down to a sea that was sloshing slightly menacingly against the cliff edge.

When I turned back, I could see the lights of the shops spilling out, illuminating the street and the railings in a damp gleam, like a Renoir, all the colours smearing into one another. It suited my mood, rather grey and a bit uniform. I supposed I should think myself lucky that I had the leisure time to mooch about and be miserable in the mist. Back in London I would have been hard at work in the flat on a typical Saturday, housework vying with marking and lesson prep, meals to be lined up for the forthcoming week to cut down on cooking time when I got in late; things, things to be done, all the time.

Here – here I had nothing to do but stand and stare at the muzzy scenery and wonder at the Impressionistic nature of it all. Also, the emptiness – where *was* everybody? I wasn't expecting Kensington levels of activity, but surely there should be people on the streets or in the harbour? Didn't you have to do things to boats? Like ponies? Always something to be tweaked or brushed down or mucked about with.

I walked slowly back towards my car, which was the only vehicle in sight, feeling a little bit as though I'd fallen into a horror film. If a distant howl travelled to me from the top of a nearby cliff, I wouldn't have been surprised, although I would have fallen over my feet in an attempt to get into the nearest shop. I stopped and looked in the illuminated window that I was passing. It was the very woolly shop that I'd met Gabriel outside a while ago. His sister's shop, I think he'd said, full of embroidered hangings and handcrafted lighthouses and things made out of wire that looked as though they might spring themselves unravelled and embed themselves in a wall twenty feet away.

I wasn't really looking in the window, more giving my eyes somewhere to rest, so when I glanced up and into the eyes of someone on the other side, it gave me a start. I took half a step back in shock and trod in a puddle.

The person inside was female, multicoloured dreadlocked and wearing a pair of dungarees that looked as though they were made out of a blanket. She'd got a pair of Doc Marten boots in bright pink laced up to her knees and a kind of orange and black artistic smock over the top, that gave the impression that she was slowly being swallowed by Sooty. My eyes hurt just looking at her.

She beckoned me to the door, which pinged open with a little bell. 'Hello,' she said, strobing her way towards me in her colourful outfit. 'You're... Katie, right? From Harvest Cottage?'

I nodded. I was a bit afraid to open my mouth in case I got possessed by the Palette From Hell.

'Gabe!' she yelled suddenly. 'Katie's here!' Then she gave me a nod and a wink, her dreadlocks swinging. 'He's upstairs in the flat, quilting. Go on up.'

'Er, I didn't...' But she was a force of nature, sweeping me towards the staircase concealed behind a little door at the back of the shop with not much more than a flick of her smock and the explosive colours of her dungarees. And 'quilting'? Did she mean making the beds?

I cautiously climbed the creaky stairs, which wound their way to the upper storey. When I got to the top, there was no landing, the staircase opened directly onto an open-plan living area, where Gabriel was hunched at a table in front of the window. He'd got a magnifying glass set up and was doing something to some fabric underneath it.

'What are you doing?' I didn't bother with greetings. Thea seemed to have taken the element of surprise and wrapped it around a brick.

'Ah.' He put the fabric down and swung the chair around to face me. 'Right. This is my day job.'

'I thought looking for locations for Keenan was your day job?'

'No, that's the job I do to keep Thea happy. She thinks I should get out more.' He looked down at the pile of fabric on the table. 'And right now I'm beginning to think she's got a point.'

'So, your day job is...?' I walked a little further into the room, mostly because I was afraid I was going to fall backwards down the stairs.

'I quilt. I make patchwork quilts.'

'We sell them online.' Thea made me jump; she'd come up behind me and I was glad I'd cleared the top of the stairs otherwise she'd have been standing several steps below me and it would have been sinister. 'There isn't room to display them in the shop. Show her, Gabe.'

'I'm not sure...' Gabriel and I said at once.

'Oh, for God's sake.' Thea sighed. 'Stop trying to out-polite each other. Look.' She picked something up from a sofa back, where it had been folded. 'This is what Gabe makes.' She shook it and the material dropped out to reveal a full-sized double quilt in shades of blue. It had been stitched so that the colours blended, squares of turquoise fading into bright blue and then down into paler blue and then through to almost grey. It was incredibly beautiful.

'Wow.' I went over for a closer look. The stitches were tiny, almost invisible, and precise. 'You made this?'

'Mmm.' He sounded as though he didn't know whether to be proud or embarrassed. 'Well, you know, it was either that or shark fishing, and I get seasick.'

'They're very popular,' Thea went on. 'Sell for a fortune.

Mum and Dad were very keen on us crafting, weren't they, Gabe?'

'I actually think they just wanted us to do something with our hands rather than try to punch each other,' he said.

'But it's beautiful.' I was awestruck. Apart from sewing buttons on and mending the odd hem, my needlework days had consisted of once making a skirt at school and sewing up plaits. The memory of that made me twitch. 'Really, Gabriel. It's gorgeous.'

'But hardly the butchest job in the world.' His tone was wry. 'Told you, the farmers' daughters are just queueing up for me. I might not be able to throw a pig two hundred metres, but I can design a quilt to match your colour scheme.'

'I've said, Gabe, you don't *have* to be butch these days. Look at Toby and Mattie. Toby's so beta male that he's practically fallen off the alphabet, and Mattie adores him. Friends of ours,' she added to me. 'And *he* earns money making balloon animals. I think quilting is really masculine compared to that.'

'Would you like to go up to the café for a coffee, Katie?' Gabriel said, standing up so suddenly that his wheeled swivel chair rotated its way across the floor. 'Anything to get away from my sister trying to make advanced needlework sound on a par with alligator wrestling.'

I was going to protest, but then I wasn't overly comfortable with Thea standing so near to me holding the quilt as though she were about to throw it over my head and smuggle me out of the building. 'That sounds lovely,' I said, eventually.

Gabriel grabbed his big black coat from the back of another chair and swung it on, advancing on me so that I had to back my way down the stairs. We reached the shop floor, leaving Thea up in the flat, making chuckling noises as though she'd just set us up on a date.

'Sorry about my sister,' he said, leading the way out of the shop and up towards the hill that stretched up out of town and formed the main street between the road to Bridport at the top of the cliff and the sea. 'She doesn't get out of Steepleton much.'

'Look,' I said, stopping suddenly. 'I feel like I upset you earlier today. You were telling me stuff and I... well, I sort of brushed you off and I shouldn't have. It was rude of me, and I'm sorry.'

He stopped too. Beads of mist hung from his hair and his coat collar; he looked as though he'd been dipped in crystal. 'There is absolutely no reason to apologise,' he said quietly. 'I was a bit of an arse. I have no right to go poking about in your life. If you want to keep control over things, well, it's nothing to do with me and I dare say you have your reasons.'

'You've told me things, though, about you, about your life.'

'You don't have to reciprocate, Katie,' he said quietly. I could see his eyes, large and dark behind his glasses, scanning over my face. 'It's not a tit-for-tat situation.'

'You basically accuse me of having a control complex, and I don't even get a right of reply?' I smiled to mitigate my words. From one of the houses that lined the street, front doors opening straight onto the pavement, I heard a burst of conversation and someone laughing, practically the first sign of life I'd come across in Steepleton proper today, apart from the colour-blocks that were Thea. Out on this street it was just Gabriel and me, the thin haze of moisture and the sound of the sea, so the reminder that other people were there too, just indoors, was somehow reassuring.

'You don't have to tell me anything,' he said. His eyes had

left my face now and he was looking up towards the top of the hill. 'Of course, you don't.'

'You've been so open with me, telling me about—' mindful of the fact that if I could hear people they could probably hear me, I lowered my voice '—how your childhood was.'

'Maybe I just needed someone to talk to. Thea's right, I don't get out much. And women don't make conversation with me, generally. Once they get the idea that I can't see and my main job is making bloody quilts for American tourists to hang on their walls.' A note of bitterness was evident now.

'You're amazingly good at it, though.' I thought about the muted, perfectly blended colours and the tiny, even stitching. 'And being good at something is attractive.'

He was focusing on my face again now, almost locked into my eyes. 'You think so? Even if it's something usually only found attractive by eighteenth-century settlers or people who've read too much *Little House on the Prairie*?'

His intensity was a little scary, out here in this deserted street. Not *him* – despite being tall and rangy, Gabriel couldn't have scared me with his almost mannered politeness and his physical distance – but, just something, there in the depths of those brown eyes made me feel as though I'd admitted to something that had blown my careful self-control open.

'You said coffee.' I broke the gaze and moved a few steps forward up the road. 'I'm freezing.' I shivered theatrically, although I was more wet than cold. 'I hope the café is open this late in the year.'

A momentary hesitation, as though he wanted to keep our previous conversation going, but then he smiled, and shook his head, little drops of water flying from his hair. 'Oh, yes. Nothing properly closes down until after Halloween.'

'You do realise how sinister that sounds, don't you? Like Steepleton is some kind of sacrificial centre.'

'Halloween or, rather, the autumn half-term, is the official end of the holiday season. You learn stuff like that when you live in a seaside town. It's when we pack away the ice-cream machines and get out the Christmas decorations.'

We'd reached the café now, the estate agent sign almost invisible behind the running condensation down the window. There weren't many houses for sale, evidently, certainly not in Steepleton. Most of the ones pictured were halfway to Dorchester, and had been for sale for a while, judging by the way the damp had wrinkled the pictures.

Maisy was typing furiously when we went in, her nails clicking over her keyboard, but she stopped as soon as she saw us. Well, as soon as she saw Gabriel, anyway.

'Wow, Gabe, twice in one year! You trying to chat me up?' Her eyes skimmed over me. 'And how's Harvest Cottage? You've not come to complain that Mr Coombes is still walking about the old place, have you?'

She must have worked on that laugh. Nobody who worked in an estate agency should have a laugh so high pitched, it sounded as though she were calling a colony of pipistrelles back to the roost.

'There's not been any sign of him,' I said, evenly. 'It's probably the vampire in the attic that's keeping him away.'

The laugh practically engraved the glass. 'Okay, two coffees, coming up, I'll just finish this...' and she rattled back on the keyboard again.

Gabriel and I sat in silence. I read the particulars of a four-bed two-bath detached house in Charmouth and wondered if it had brambles in the pantry and single glazing. It made me remember Luc's ancestral home, which also had single glazing and a plethora of invertebrates, but was a few centuries behind and a dozen bedrooms ahead of Harvest Cottage. It also had an ancient Roman villa converted into a guest cottage and a swimming pool, while I only had Patrick and, now, Granny Mary as additional extras.

Sometimes I missed being rich. Right up until I remembered Luc's behaviour, his casual affairs, his disappearances, when suddenly living in poor rural isolation didn't look so bad.

When I looked up, Gabriel was watching me. It was a disconcerting look, as though he was trying to sum me up. I looked away again. There was a poster in the window advertising the forthcoming Halloween fête and disco, decorated with lurid pumpkin faces and witches' hats. 'Has Steepleton always had a Halloween fair?' I asked. 'Even when you were young?'

'Oy, I'm thirty-two, not prehistoric, thank you,' he said, without rancour. 'Yes, they had invented Halloween when I was young. We used to have a procession down the main street, everyone in costume.' His voice went a bit dreamy. 'I was always a ghost. Thea used to be something like Hecate, something precise. I just got general "sheet over the head and eyeholes". Then there'd be a do in the village hall down the street there.' He nodded towards the grey building that had evidently been a village school in a previous life and was now reincarnated as the general centre for all indoor activities. 'Now it's more like stalls and games, pumpkin carving and all that. And the disco, of course.'

'I used to love a good disco,' I said dreamily and mumbled a quick refrain of 'Who Let the Dogs Out' complete with arm movement before I realised it was no longer cutting-edge music.

'I don't think they let you go if you're over nineteen,' Gabriel said. 'It's "a bit sad" apparently. Shame, cos I love a good dance.'

'We could have our own disco,' I said suddenly. 'Put some of the old hits on, boogie round the kitchen, drink WKD...'

'Throw up in a hedge, realise your lift has gone without you and get caught trying to ride a cow home,' he finished. 'No? Just me, then. Rural life has a lot to answer for.'

'No, we could.' I began to warm to my theme. 'Poppy thinks that she deserves all the fun, all the pumpkin faces and the candles and the dancing and all that, but, really, why can't *I* have some fun too? Why shouldn't we be allowed to have a party?'

'Because we are old and boring and creak alarmingly trying to dance to Avicii. Thanks, Mais.' Gabriel took the coffees. 'Besides, someone has to stay sober enough to referee the teenage fights.'

'And I will have to drive Poppy here, there and everywhere.' I sighed, my mood deflating with the foam on my coffee. 'You're right. Sometimes I hate being grown up.'

'It's not so bad,' he said. 'Nobody's trying to throw my clothes in the swimming pool any more, for starters. And the calling of names gets done a lot more quietly.'

I looked at him over my coffee. 'Again, you're right.'

'Ah, come on, I bet your teenage years were full of, what? Pony clubs and shows? I've seen you with Patrick. You've got that sort of "capable, nothing fazes me" practicality of someone who was brought up on hay nets and horse rugs.'

'Something like that.' I knew my voice sounded tight, but I'd taken quite a mouthful of hot coffee.

'I far prefer adulthood,' he said, quieter still, stretching his hand around his cup. 'Childhood in a small village in rural

Dorset is not the carefree idyll that people from the city seem to think it is.'

'Childhood can be tough wherever you grow up.'

In the window, Blu-Tack gave up in the face of the damp and some of the house posters peeled down to collect in a pool on the window ledge. Maisy gave a little shriek and ran over to start trying to press them into place again.

'And that's why you are so careful with Poppy? Are you trying to give her the perfect childhood?' Gabriel wasn't looking at me. He was flexing his fingers, those long fingers that I now realised were honed by hours of careful, precise stitching.

'There's no such thing as the perfect childhood,' I said briskly. 'Particularly for teenagers. They are predisposed towards dissatisfaction – it's the thing that drives them to leave home and do different stuff. I'd guess a perfect child-hood isn't always a good thing anyway – it's going to be all downhill from there.'

I could see my hand, lying on the table. Compared it to his. My hand was soft from years of writing on whiteboards, typing up reports, soothing a child to sleep. I hadn't really looked at my hands for years. I wondered when they'd got so pale and clean.

In my pocket my phone rang. 'Sorry, I'd better take it. It's Poppy.'

He inclined his head and carried on drinking the coffee, while Poppy informed me that she'd finished her shift in the café, and although Karen had said she could stay on she wanted to come home and do 'stuff' so could I pick her up?

'I'd better bring her home. She'll have homework. Although mostly she seems to be planning for the Halloween do. And I really ought to go back to make sure that Granny

Mary is... well, I should make sure she knows where everything is.'

'The crew are all up there. She's not on her own.'

'Then maybe I should be there to protect them from her. No, sorry,' I added quickly. 'I'm sure she's lovely really, when you get to know her.' I drained the rest of my coffee and pushed my chair back.

'Granny Mary is the epitome of "what you see is what you get", but she's very kind and somewhere underneath her incredible collection of rock band T-shirts beats a heart of gold.' He stayed sitting. 'I'll come over and check on her tomorrow. If that's all right with you, of course.'

'Well, yes, why wouldn't it be?'

He gave me a very steady look from those dark eyes. 'I was worried that I might have crossed a line during our previous conversation,' he said. 'And you might want to keep your distance.'

'You're coming to check on an elderly lady, not force your way into my bedroom.' I picked up my bag and phone. 'And no lines have been crossed, honestly. As for distance, well, sometimes that's for the best, don't you agree?'

When I left the coffee shop he was still sitting there, arms stretched across the table and his mug cupped between his hands. He didn't move, as though his mind was focused somewhere else, and my last glimpse of him was rippled at the edges through the fogged glass of the window. Just sitting.

10

That night a wind blew in from the sea.

I lay in bed, with the windows rattling on the side of the house that faced the coast and the trees that lined the lane swooshing and sighing dramatically. I was almost sure I could hear surf booming off the base of the cliffs, but that could have been my imagination.

My bedroom door creaked open and a sliver of light from the landing hit the bed. 'Mum?' Not quite a whisper, not quite a normal volume.

'What's up, Pops?' I struggled to sit up. 'Can't you sleep?'

'It's noisy.'

'It's just the wind. If you fold up some paper and shove it between the window and the frame, it stops the windows rattling.'

Poppy came inside, hesitantly. Luc had never allowed her into our bedroom at night, unless she was ill, and the habit of uncertainty had stuck. Even though, once she was over five, he was hardly ever at home at night. 'I'm scared.'

Backlit by the swaying landing bulb, in her slightly too small pyjamas, she looked so young. On school nights she put her hair up into a bun to stop it getting tangled, but at weekends she slept with it loose, which made her look even younger. Fourteen. A hell of an age.

'Do you want to come in with me tonight?' I flipped the edge of the duvet back.

No second invitation was needed and she clambered in, taking a customary two-thirds of the bed, and eight-ninths of the duvet. 'It's just so *dark*!' Still whispering, although we were the only two in the house and both, demonstrably, already awake.

She was right. I could almost feel the darkness pressing against the walls of the house, kept at bay only by the landing light, which I kept on at night to prevent me from falling down the stairs during a nocturnal trip to the bathroom. The light made the darkness seem even darker; there wasn't a shred of moonlight and the stars were invisible behind a cloud cover. The trees were just darker patches.

'We're just not used to it. After London,' I whispered back. 'We'll get used to it.'

A pause. I could hear her breathing and it was nowhere near the settled deep breaths of someone falling asleep. 'Could we get a dog?'

'It wouldn't be fair.' I stroked her hair. 'Once I get a job, hopefully in the spring term, a dog would be at home by itself all day.'

I had a quick memory of childhood, coming home from school to be greeted by a cacophony of barking spaniels, greeting me in the hallway with their floppy ears, cold noses pressing into my schoolbag and warm licks of happy acknowledgement. The weight of a sleeping dog on my feet. The warning growl when strangers approached the door. The sense of being protected.

'Maybe we could think about a cat, though. Or two, to keep each other company.'

'Mmmmm.' She snuggled down, pulling her more-than-fair-share of duvet up over her shoulders. 'Cats are good.' Then, drowsily, 'I really like Rory, Mum.'

I absolutely didn't know how to reply to that, so I stayed quiet. Let her think I'd fallen asleep. And, after a few moments of wriggling, her breathing settled, and she was asleep. I stayed awake a little longer, listening to the roar of the wind in the high branches, the tapping of smaller twigs against windows and the occasional wind-carried cry of an owl. I could almost imagine I could hear the dragging steps of Mr Coombes along the hallway, and silently cursed Maisy and her overactive imagination as I pulled the pillow over my head and dug myself deeper under my fraction of the duvet.

When I woke up the next morning, Poppy was gone. But then, the grey light filtering in told me I'd overslept again, as though my body was trying to make up for all those incredibly early mornings over the years. With no external noise to wake me, and my alarm not set, I woke when I was ready, probably for the first time in – how long?

It was another chilly morning with a gentle sluice of rain falling, so I pulled a fleece on over my pyjamas and went downstairs through the clammy air. The wood of the bannister rail was slippery with the damp, and I decided we'd have to light the wood-burner today, logs or no logs. If I didn't keep the inside of the cottage warmer than the outside, we'd be up to our knees in mould before winter, and a little bit of heat might keep the woodlice at bay.

The stone floor of the kitchen was cold, so I stepped into my slip-on rubber shoes in the doorway. We'd brought slippers, but our slim-soled cosmetic footwear that had been perfectly suitable for underfloor-heated London flats was absolutely useless in the face of the brittle old-air cold that rose up from the flags. We'd acquired defensive shoes very quickly.

The kitchen smelled of toast and the kettle was still steaming. Poppy must have had Sunday breakfast alone. I examined the bread, in case it had already gone green, and then popped it in the toaster and started to make tea. 'Pops!' I called up through the ceiling to her room. 'Do you want more tea?'

No reply. Not even the thud of feet moving about. I peered into the living room, where the wood-burner stood invitingly loaded with fuel, but she wasn't there either. I opened the back door.

Through the glaze of rain I could see Patrick pulling at his hay net under the newly leafless apple tree. Most of the remaining leaves, and the apples that had hung from the unreachable branches, had fallen in the night's gales, and lay like a mosaic beneath his hooves. Over at the caravan smoke puffed out of the metal chimney. I decided to make a mug of tea for Granny Mary, then hoped that she wouldn't think I was going to make her tea every morning. But I made it anyway, and put a few chocolate biscuits on a plate. Took them off, reasoning that I didn't want her to get too comfortable in my orchard, then put them back on again; she was an old lady who'd been ill. Then I wavered, in case she'd expect biscuits, decided I was being silly, and before I could change my mind again I went out, gathering my fleece at the neck against the penetrating rain.

I knocked on the van door and, to my astonishment, it was opened by Poppy. Inside the van sat Granny Mary and Gabriel.

'Are you playing Sardines?' I asked.

'There's plenty of room. Romanies raise families in these vans,' Granny Mary replied, eyeing the biscuits. 'Those for us?'

I put the plate on the table, handed her the mug, which she added to the considerable collection on the table in front of her.

'Gabriel is showing me how to stitch,' Poppy said. 'Sharon gave me this red dress, and Gabriel's showing me how to do the gold embroidery for my Cersei costume.'

Gabriel had his needle threaded and a swathe of fabric on his knee. He looked a bit embarrassed to be caught in the act again. 'I've drawn the design on in tailor's chalk,' he said, to Poppy. 'If you do those stitches I've shown you over the top, I reckon it will be good enough for Halloween. If you want anything more detailed, I can make you a costume, but it takes a while. We've only got a couple of weeks before the disco, so this will have to do for now.'

Granny Mary ate a biscuit. It was warm and snug in the van. The stove was belting out heat and there was a smell of something cooking in a pan. In the grey rainy light, the paint-work shone, more muted than by bright sun, and it all felt very cosy. Much nicer than the cottage, in fact. Mary and Gabriel were sitting at the table on the low bench seat, Poppy was perched on a brightly painted stool. I hovered in the doorway.

'Come in and sit down,' Granny Mary ordered. 'You're making the place look untidy standing there. Here.' Another stool shot out from under the table and I sat, lower down than they were on their bench, feeling like an adult at primary school parents' evening.

'So I'm wearing the red dress and Gabriel's showed me how to sew it up so it's got these big sleeve things, and I've got that huge belt that looks like a corset and I'm going to wear my heels and Rory's got this necklace thing that he bought from Exeter this one time that's just like Cersei's, and I'm going to do my hair all up...' She pulled her hair up and back and demonstrated, all breathless excitement and wide-eyed anticipation. 'And it's going to be so-o-o-o-o cool.'

'And breathe,' said Granny Mary, but with a hint of amusement in her voice. 'Surprised you don't run out of words, way you carry on.'

If I had said that, Poppy would have rounded on me and accused me of trying to spoil her fun, or of criticising the way she spoke or something. From Granny Mary, apparently though, it was a huge joke.

'You should *so* come!' Poppy addressed her. 'You could get Patrick to pull the van down to the car park and you could tell fortunes!'

Granny Mary side-eyed her. 'Young lady, I am not a charlatan.'

Poppy looked blank. 'It means a fake,' I said.

'Oh. Nah, everyone would know it was just made up. You could have a crystal ball and one of those scarf things and just tell everyone you could see someone tall, dark and handsome in their future. It'd be *ace*!'

Granny Mary's eyes flicked over to Gabriel, quietly stitching away, and then on to me. 'Tall, dark and handsome,' she said to no one in particular.

'Yes. Oh, go on, Granny Mary! You'd be brill.'

'Ach, I'm a bit old for play-acting, child. You'll be fine without me. There's always plenty to do at the Halloween fair.' Mary ate another biscuit. I watched Gabriel's hands, capable and long-fingered, laying down fine gold thread work.

'That's beautiful,' I said.

'I did this bit!' Poppy held up a swathe of fabric from the other end of the dress. 'Gabriel showed me how.'

'Since when did you do sewing?' I asked her.

'Mémé taught me, a couple of summers ago.' She picked at the fabric. 'Mum, for my birthday, could I have a sewing machine? And a pony?'

It figured that Luc's mother would have had Poppy sewing. It was what she considered a good girl should do competently. A good wife should sew and cook. The other things she should do for her husband I devoutly hoped had not been mentioned, let alone lessons given. But in Mémé's favour, she never considered that a woman should hoover or iron – that was what staff were for.

'We'll see,' I said. 'About the sewing machine. No ponies though.'

Granny Mary caught my eye again. She had a particularly intense stare, as though behind those blue eyes was an awful lot of brain activity. I stared back, daring her to say anything, but she just finished the last biscuit off the plate, and turned the laser-stare out of the window.

Gabriel tied a knot and bit the end of the thread. 'There. That's as much as I can do now. You can finish the rest off – you've got a fortnight.'

Poppy gave a little squeak. 'Thanks, Gabe! It's amazing!'

Gabe? I thought.

'No problem.' He smiled, that wide, eye-crinkling smile, and his face fell into the easy handsomeness that his glasses only accentuated. 'And tell Rory that if he's got any problems with his costume, he can run it over to me next week and I'll see what I can do.'

Poppy blinked at him. She looked as though she was caught between kissing him as a child would, or giving him a coquettish look from under her lashes, but she came down on the side of youth and flung her arms around his neck. 'You're *brilliant*,' she said, seized the dress and dashed out of the van with it bundled up under her jacket against the rain, presumably to phone Rory.

'I'm brilliant,' Gabriel said, slightly smugly.

'You burn with the light of a thousand suns, m'dear.' Granny Mary began fussing the mugs together. 'But don't take it to heart.'

'Well, nobody is usually that impressed with my sewing. It's nice to be appreciated without someone saying, "It's not bad, for a *bloke*," like having a pe... I mean, like being male means I should do huge stitches like something from an autopsy.'

'Most of the top fashion designers are men,' I said, wishing I'd brought the biscuit packet with me from the kitchen.

'Most top chefs are men, but I can't do much fancy stuff,' he replied, reasonably enough. 'Although I did once make a decent chocolate cake from a Nigella cookbook.'

'And anyway, *I'm* impressed with your sewing. It's amazing. That quilt that Thea showed me, I'd have no idea even where to start with something like that.'

Granny Mary fumbled behind her for a moment and pulled something off the bed. 'This is one of his,' she said, spreading it across the part of the table that wasn't occupied by mugs. 'An early one, I think, Gabe?'

He acknowledged it with a tilt of his head. 'I'm a bit more even with the stitching now. And I use an extra layer of wadding, makes it a bit fuller.'

This quilt was, in keeping with the rest of the inside of the van, multicoloured. Reds and oranges competed with browns and greens, like a forest fire in fabric. Unlike the shades-of-blue one I'd seen at Thea's, there was nothing subtle about this; it glowed as though it had its own, internal light source.

'It's glorious,' I said.

'Better be, it was bloody expensive.' Mary sniffed and poked it back onto the bed. 'You must be making a fortune on those things.'

'Well, they take a long time to make, and the fabric can be pricey, so not as much as you'd think.'

'But you've got a house.'

Gabriel frowned. 'Well, yes, but with a mortgage. It's not like quilting is going to make me a millionaire, Mary, and you can't crochet property.'

She sniffed again. 'Houses are overrated.'

My eyes met his and I had to stifle the urge to giggle. We shared a complicit eye-roll. 'Right, well, now I've checked that you're all right, I ought to get back to Steepleton. They aren't filming today but Keenan wants a meeting to check up on some timings and I've said I'll be there.' Gabriel stood up and the van instantly looked smaller.

'Off you toddle,' Mary said, equably.

'And I need to go and light the log-burner.' I turned to follow him out of the door. 'The cottage is starting to feel the autumn coming in.'

'Just you wait a minute,' Mary said, and her voice was suddenly stronger. 'I want a quick word.'

It was like being addressed by the head, being back at work. I wondered what I'd done. Mary sat quietly for a while; we heard Gabriel saying goodbye to Patrick and then the sound of him climbing over the gate. Gabriel, obviously. Patrick wouldn't have needed to climb the gate; he'd go straight through it like a tank.

'You need to tell him,' Mary said, once the gate noises had died away. 'It's not fair otherwise.'

'*What?*' I jumped to my feet, almost unaware of the action until I felt the van sway.

Mary wasn't looking at me, she was gazing towards the stove, where the fire burned low. 'He's halfway to falling in love with you and I think you know that.'

'I know no such thing!' I grabbed the edge of the table. 'We're just – we just...' I tailed off, unable to finish the sentence.

'Don't you be disingenuous with me, madam. You know perfectly well what he's doing with all that "sewing isn't very macho" thing; he's checking up to see what you think about it. And you're giving it the "fashion designers are men".' She put on a high-pitched voice for that, which I assumed was supposed to be me. 'You like him back. So, he needs to know.'

'Do I? Like him back?' I stared at the door Gabriel had recently gone out of, almost as though I could see his image embossed on it. Tall, dark and handsome. Of course.

'Your pupils go so big you look like you've had an eye examination whenever you talk to him, Now, sit down again, unless you're going to fetch some more biscuits.'

I sat down on the little stool that put my chin level with

the tabletop. I had the feeling that Granny Mary rather enjoyed talking down to me.

'I met Luc when I was doing my year living in France.' I looked at my hands in my lap so as not to see her expression. 'We got married and had Poppy before I finished my training, and then I went into teaching.' Now I looked up. 'There's never been anyone else. And I was *so young*...'

'I don't mean that, as well you know. Your inexperience with men is probably a good match with Gabe.'

I wondered if Granny Mary knew about Gabriel going out with Karen. I had the feeling that 'inexperience' and 'Karen' did not go together.

'He needs to know about you being Katherine Bryant.'

Now I looked up. 'No.'

'You can't base a relationship on lying by omission, Katie.' Her voice was much more gentle now, the voice I'd heard her using to Patrick. 'It explains so much about you. Don't you think he deserves to know?'

'No!' I said again. Then, 'It's not that he doesn't *deserve* to know. It's just that that part of my life is nothing to do with me now.'

'If that young man falls in love with you without knowing who you really are, then it isn't really love, is it? I bet he's told you about himself, about how it's been, with the blindness maybe coming on and all.'

I thought about the other things Gabriel had told me. About the bullying, the hiding from school, dropping out of the swimming team. He'd wanted me to know him, warts and all. While I was still hiding behind being Katie Gerauld, divorced wife and mother. 'Yes, he has,' I said quietly.

'Well, then. Even if you think it's not who you are now, it explains a lot about the way you are, especially with your daughter. If he knows about your past, it stops you looking quite so bonkers in the present, don't you think?'

Mary stood up and slowly began gathering the mugs from the table, putting them into a little plastic bowl on the side.

I took a deep breath. 'So what about you, then, Mary? What's your story?'

'Deflection won't get you anywhere, Katie.' She still spoke gently. 'But, since you asked... I worked too hard. Top-flight microbiology. We did a lot of good, but – well, it doesn't come with much of a social life. I always promised myself, when I retired I'd buy a little caravan and do some travelling and, here we are.' She rinsed the mugs and set them to drain on the shelf above the fire, with her back to me. 'I sold a very nice house in Bracknell, as it happens, to buy Patrick and the van and keep us on the road. Not such a bad life.' She sniffed and then said again, more dreamily, 'Yes. Not such a bad life.'

Then that bright blue stare switched back on and laser-sliced its way around the van until it came to rest on me again. 'You tell him, girl.'

'Or what?' I felt a bit stronger now, almost as though having that little glimpse into her world had given me another perspective. 'Or you will?'

'Oh, no.' She wiped both hands down the front of the Motörhead T-shirt that she was wearing today. 'No, that's not my style. But if you don't tell him, it'll be between you always. And he's too nice a boy for that. Besides, he might look thicker than a rag rug, but he's going to start to wonder, don't you think? About why you moved to the back of beyond, Dorsetshire, from London, where you had a job and good schools and all the opportunities for your daughter? You trying to protect her from everything. All those things she doesn't know... He's a clever lad, our Gabriel. He'll be thinking about it.'

I could almost feel it now. The huge gulf that lay between who I'd been then and who I was now, and all the things that had fallen into that trench.

'How do I tell him?' I said, speaking to the violently coloured curtains that fluttered against the tiny window. 'How do I tell someone that I killed my father?'

11

I stared out of my bedroom window. A few days had passed since I'd spoken to Mary, and life had intervened since then. Plus, I'd deliberately kept out of her way. I didn't want a repeat of that conversation. Now I was watching Keenan directing a horse-wrangler, who was wrangling Patrick – a horse that didn't so much need wrangling as resuscitating – through the gateway in full harness. They'd moved the caravan out into the lane and were, apparently, pretending that this was the first arrival at Serial Killer Cottage. There had already been shots of Patrick pulling the caravan up and down the lane. Granny Mary had insisted, according to Keenan, on driving, so there had been many cut-away shots and much careful framing so as not to reveal that the van was being controlled by a little old lady rather than Killer Peter.

Patrick looked different in harness, like meeting someone you know socially in a work setting. The big bridle with the blinkers and the gleaming brass fittings made his head look smaller and finer boned and he'd had a really good groom. His mane and tail flowed out behind him as he trotted, picking up his enormous feet as though he were trotting through tin tacks. He would occasionally stretch out his neck and snort, as though he wasn't quite fit enough for the work he was doing, and the wrangler would have to stop and walk him quietly for a while. Patrick had gone soft during the weeks in my orchard.

I had retreated to my room to cut faces out of pumpkins, as instructed by Poppy, who wanted them for the Halloween fair, two lanterns, one each for her and Rory to carry. So far I'd ruined three, and had to drive up to Bridport for more supplies; my room was full of pumpkin innards, newspaper and squinty-eyed pumpkins with off-centre mouths. Carving faces was not turning out to be a latent talent of mine, although I had discovered a hitherto unsuspected ability to swear very loudly and curse the god of squashes and gourds. I'd watched more YouTube videos than I cared to remember, and they all made it look so easy. They definitely didn't show the blood and plasters or the splatty-faced failures. There was one currently resting on my dressing table that looked as though I'd punched a melon.

I sighed and sucked at yet another cut finger.

There was a knock at the door. 'I've brought you a cup of tea,' Gabriel said from the other side of the woodwork. 'You've not been on set for a while and I just wanted to check you were okay. And by "you" I mean "we" because you seem to be avoiding me.'

I opened the door. 'Yes, thank you. Sorry, I've just been...'

'Wow. Are you going to stick pins in them?' Gabriel came in and stared at a particularly lopsided carving attempt on the dressing table. 'Like voodoo dolls of people with really big heads?'

I stared with him. 'I think anyone who looks like this has

already got enough problems.' A badly cut piece of mouth slowly caved inwards under the weight of our gaze, and flopped inside the pumpkin with a hollow, wet sound. 'It looks like I've found whatever the opposite of a niche in life is. But I promised Poppy, so...' I shrugged '... here I am.'

'Here.' Gabriel handed me a mug and put his own down carefully on a piece of newspaper. 'Drink that and I'll see what I can do.'

'You carve pumpkins?'

He flashed me a dark glance. 'I was brought up in rural Dorset with appalling eyesight and half the local boys tracking my every outdoor movement. I'm a dab hand at anything you can do indoors in front of your family.' He looked at my collection of knives. 'Using these, I'm surprised you haven't cut yourself to ribbons.'

I held up the hand not embracing the tea. Several soaked plasters adorned my fingers. 'I have. I didn't think it would be so difficult!'

He winced. 'Don't you *have* pumpkins in London?'

'Yes, but I always bought them pre-carved from a lovely artist who lived in our block. Poppy was usually at parties, so we just used them as a table centrepiece.'

Gabriel shook his head. Then he took off his jacket, rolled up the sleeves of the black sweater he had on underneath, and bent close to a so-far untouched pumpkin. 'Get me an apple corer, a citrus peeler and a black marker pen, stat,' he said. 'We'll have this man on his feet again in no time.'

I fled down to the kitchen and pulled out the cutlery drawer. The apple corer was right at the front; we'd eaten a lot of apples since moving here. The citrus peeler was right at the back, behind some other exotic devices that I'd only brought here because I'd bought them and I was damned if Luc's new girlfriend was going to get custody of them. Then I stopped, hand still delved deep among the pasta servers and steak tenderisers as the realisation hit me that Luc's girlfriends had probably been in the flat quite frequently. I'd worked long hours during term-time, and Poppy had also been at school. Luc, floating about on the income from his family's investments and wine business, had had all day to bring his current girlfriend home.

I wondered why I'd put up with it for so long. I'd tried, of course I had, but Luc had shrugged that particularly French shrug and rattled off something that even I hadn't understood. And he'd been there for Poppy, for Christmases and birthdays, with lavish presents, and he'd taken her off to the family chateau for holidays. It was me that he'd let down.

'Any sign of that apple corer?' Gabriel's voice came down through the floorboards. 'Only I'm losing our patient!'

I realised my fingers were white on the carefully carved handle of my Harrods corer. Torn between wanting to plunge it into my husband's congenitally unfaithful heart, and the realisation that we should have split up years before we actually did. That 'staying together for Poppy' had probably done more harm than good.

'Keep him breathing, I'm on my way!' I called back, and grasped the implements. Granny Mary must have got further inside my head than I'd thought, with her questions about why I had come to rural Dorset. She was right, of course. We could have bought another, smaller flat in London. Maybe not in as fashionable an area, maybe with more of a walk to the Tube, but we could have stayed.

My heart raced as I imagined London, and I found myself bent over the sink, feeling sick. Only the creaking overhead as

Gabriel walked to the landing to shout down the stairs again pulled me back.

'Oh, and if you've got any cobwebs down there...'

Cobwebs? The incongruity of the request jolted me out into the hallway. 'Cobwebs?'

'Yes, I just nicked my finger on this knife.'

With my armful of equipment, I went back up to my room, where Gabriel was standing holding his finger. 'Your knives are dangerous,' he said.

'Cobwebs?' I said again. 'I think there are some in the bathroom. I try, I really do, but the spiders have squatters' rights, apparently.' I opened the door to the bathroom, glad that I'd had a quick tidy round when the film crew arrived. It wasn't exactly acres of gleaming porcelain, but it wasn't engrained or a floor full of dirty knickers either.

'Ah, yes. Got one.' Gabriel reached up and swiped down a small web that had been nestling blamelessly above the cistern. He wrapped it around the narrow slice that I could see at the base of his first finger, then looked at me. I was boggling.

'Is this some kind of ancient magic?'

'Don't be daft. Spiders' webs have this stuff on them that makes blood coagulate. A clean web will stop a small cut from bleeding.' He waggled the finger at me. 'See?'

All I could really see was a fine grey mesh and a little bit of blood. 'Are you sure?'

'Yep, native knowledge. Only works on very small cuts, of course. If you lop your leg off then it's not much use. Unless you've got Shelob living in your basement. Shelob. Huge great spider from *The Lord of the Rings*?' He seemed mystified at my puzzled expression. 'Blimey, and I thought *I* needed to get out more.'

In the bedroom he'd made a start on one of the pumpkin faces. 'You did all this while I was downstairs?'

'Er, yes. I tried to persuade the fairies to do it, but they weren't having it. Why?'

He'd started carving out a copy of the *Scream* face. It already looked amazing, and backlit with a candle or torch it was going to be incredible. I stared at it for a moment, then over at my wonky-eyed, gap-toothed primary-school attempts. 'Gabriel,' I said slowly, 'you are wonderful.'

'I have my moments.' He didn't turn round, he just kept his head down, bent over the pumpkin.

I remembered Granny Mary saying that he was halfway to being in love with me. His back view and dismissive words didn't lend much credence to that. And then I remembered what else she'd said. That in order to let him in, I'd need to tell him about myself. About my past.

'I'm just going to check on the crew.' I put my mug, the corer and peeler down beside him. 'They might need... err... something.'

Without waiting for him to reply, I fled back down the stairs again, pulled my big coat from the hook in the hallway and opened the kitchen door to the wall of rain.

Granny Mary was sitting complacently inside the van in the lay-by, with the top half of the door open and her face sort of thrust through the gap, watching her pony being led in and out of the gateway, while Keenan and a cameraman who looked soggy and disgruntled moved around.

'Okay, I think that's it,' Keenan said, pulling his hat off and running a hand through damp hair. 'I'll go through the shots. There's bound to be something in there we can use.'

The man who was pretending to be the man who was acting the serial killer, because the actor was off doing his documentary and needed a stand-in, gave a sigh and let go of Patrick's bridle. The equipment men hurried to pack up the various bits and pieces and coil cables, while Patrick, currently half in the gateway, rested a hoof and let his head droop. He looked bored and wet, despite continuity's best efforts at keeping him dry.

Horse wrangler started untacking, while Keenan debriefed his squad and I went over to see Mary.

'Where's Gabriel gone?' She poked her head through the window to peer out at me.

'He's upstairs, carving a pumpkin.' I jerked my head towards the bedroom window. The light was on in the room, spilling down into the garden and highlighting the rain sheeting onto the bushes.

'Got him in your bedroom already?' Mary let out a laugh that sounded like an involuntary spasm. 'That's promising.'

I refused to rise to her bait. 'This weather is dreadful, isn't it?' I hoped she wasn't going to agree and ask to move into the cottage, but then her van was probably warmer and drier.

'Forecast to carry on too. We've got gales coming in from the west and they're talking about moving the Halloween fair into the tourist office so it doesn't get washed away.' Mary settled her arms on the ledge, the eaves of the van keeping her dry. 'Going to be a right storm.'

I instantly thought about Poppy walking around Steepleton with the waves lashing up over the sea wall, teenagers larking about, people being swept into the sea, and wondered if I could persuade her to only go for the disco being safely held in the village hall. I leaned against the side of the van as my legs went weak.

'It...' I started, but didn't know how to go on. Mary wasn't a person I'd choose to go to for reassurance. 'Patrick did well, didn't he?' I settled on the most non-controversial topic I could think of. 'He's going to be a real star when this goes out.'

'He's a good lad. Nice and steady.' Mary eyeballed me again. 'And they've filmed the van too – going to be inundated with offers to buy it, Keenan reckons.'

'Would you sell?' I mentally ran through her options. Wonderful though the caravan was, it wouldn't raise enough money to buy a house in this part of the world. She wouldn't want to move in with me, would she? Or Gabriel? I thought about Thea's flat, with those steep stairs, and dismissed it.

'I'll die in this van,' she said, with a slight note of satisfaction. 'I've done my time living in houses and I prefer to be here, where I can open the door and smell nature.'

I bit my lip so as not to point out that I could open *my* door and smell nature, if, by nature, you meant a wet horse and a lot of mud.

'So you wouldn't sell?' I relaxed a bit.

'Course not.' Mary resettled her arms and watched me getting dripped on by the van roof. 'You ought to go and check that young Gabriel hasn't got out of bed and run off, y'know. He's a patient lad, but he won't wait forever.'

I wanted to retort that she could stuff her old-person-wisdom, and I didn't care whether Gabriel ran off or not, it was nothing to me one way or the other. But then I thought of that concentrated dark gaze and those long fingers, and kept my mouth shut. I turned away, hearing another of her snorted laughs behind me, and went over to Keenan.

'We're done for the day, I think,' he said. 'Not much more to do up here actually. Maybe a few pick-up shots when we get Peter back after the documentary, but we're pretty well finished, I think. You'll come down and see us in Steeple-ton?' He sounded rather forlorn. 'We'll have a wrap party when we finish filming this series, and everyone's invited. Plus, Larch quite likes you and that's rare enough to go down in the annals, so if you wanted to come over and just hang out, chat, eat in the catering van...? To be honest, I'd be grateful to anyone who could keep Larch happy and from murdering Davin, so we'd be absolutely delighted to see you on set.'

He took off the flat cap he was wearing, which was doing nothing to keep the rain off his head, and ran his hands through his hair again.

I quite liked Larch. She was dippy and wafty and a bit given to patronising comments, but she was innocently sweet and reminded me of Poppy rather a lot. 'Of course, I will.' I patted his arm reassuringly. 'I'm at quite a loose end myself until I get another teaching job. The money you've paid to film here has been keeping us afloat this long though.'

Keenan shuddered. 'Don't mention anything floating, please. We've had some shockers of storms while we've been here. The other Christmas Davin and Tansy got washed into the seal Don't want that again.'

I made a mental note to keep Poppy at home when the storm struck. Tansy and Davin might have survived, but... I shuddered. I might have to make arrangements to barricade her in her room though.

I left them packing up their gear and went back inside. 'The crew are just leaving,' I said up the stairs, 'if you need to go with them.'

Gabriel appeared on the landing again, half in shadow. 'I've just about cracked this first pumpkin.' He leaned down. 'So if it's okay with you I'll stay a bit longer. I can always walk down later – it's really not that far if you go over the fields.'

'I'll drive you back,' I found myself offering. 'It'll be getting dark and it's raining. Plus, you're doing me a favour by covering up my lack of artistic ability.'

Gabriel came down the first two stairs. 'I'm quite used to the dark and I haven't dissolved up to now,' he said, reasonably.

That made me go quiet.

'But I'll take another tea, if you're making,' he called over his shoulder. 'And I might just bring these downstairs now, if the crew don't need the living room.'

'Of course.'

I dashed into the living room, where the damp atmosphere was making the walls shine, and lit the log-burner. I'd taken to cleaning it out and re-laying it every morning after Poppy went to school, then leaving it unlit until the evening when she came back. There were logs in the little shed, where I kept Patrick's hay, but not nearly enough to see us through a winter. I'd been trying to eke them out, and leaving the fire unlit during the day had seemed a good option.

When Gabriel came in, carrying two pumpkins, a wad of newspaper and a cutlery-inspired arsenal, the flames were blazing up in the log-burner, I'd pulled the sofa closer to the fire and rearranged the cushions to make the room look more hospitable. Poppy did her homework in here in the evenings, and spread herself along the sofa to watch Netflix, so it felt more like her room than mine. I was usually incarcerated in the kitchen, where the stove kept the place above freezing and the woodlice kept me company.

'It's nice in here.' Gabriel sat on the grey wool rug in front of the fire, paper spread out. 'Homely.'

I'd done what I could with our rescued London stuff. Long beige curtains hung at the window that looked out over the overgrown front garden and the gate, and the enormous sofa took up most of the floorspace, perched with a side table on top of a multicoloured carpet offcut that I'd bought in Bridport. Around the edges, the bare wood floor was still visible, which made the carpet look like a life raft onto which I'd piled all the furniture.

'Homely? Does it? Only if "home" is a cottage in the woods, wicked witch optional.' I began rearranging the cushions, feeling self-conscious suddenly about my London things in this rural setting. Keenan had loved filming in here, he'd said it was 'offbeat', by which I supposed he meant that it looked like the sort of furnishings that a serial killer would be comfortable with, and I wasn't sure how I felt about that. Homely was a step up.

'It all just kind of works.' Gabriel waved a hand. 'It fits.'

'We had to take the sofa in through the window.'

'That's not what I mean.' He looked up at me. 'Why are you so nervous, Katie?'

Behind its reinforced door, the log-burner banged as wood fell.

'Nervous? Am I?' I had to stop myself from giving a little giggle.

He did the sideways head-tilt again. It made his hair fall across his face, and I found myself really wanting to push my hands through that soft, dark drift. There was a grace to the way he bent over the pumpkins on the rug, almost as if he were in a very seasonal yoga pose, curved and curled and catlike. It brought his face close to the carving and made his glasses slide down his nose a little and I was finding it hard to look away.

'It's just something Granny Mary said. About the weather.' And before I knew it I was perched on the edge of the sofa, with him sitting on the edge of the wood-burner plinth, back to the fire, and I was trying to explain how I was afraid for Poppy, being in the village in a storm.

He listened quietly. Apart from turning the as yet uncarved pumpkin over in his hands, he didn't move, and he didn't keep stopping me to suggest things in the way Luc used to do. It felt odd, being uninterrupted, so I might have gone on for longer than was wise.

'You worry a lot about Poppy, don't you?'

'I'm her *mother*! It's basically all worry from the moment they finish stitching you up and ask if you'd like a cup of tea!' My eyes felt very hot and I took some deep breaths. I didn't want to cry in front of Gabriel.

He let the pumpkin roll away and moved up to sit next to me on the sofa. 'Katie,' he said gently, 'the Halloween fair is for Steepleton people. It's not going to be full of incomers and holidaymakers.'

'I know! But I'm a teacher, I know what teenagers can be like, all showing off and trying to be more daring than each other. It only takes one to decide to jump on the sea wall, getting his friends to record him to stick it on YouTube, and the next thing...' I tailed off, my inner eye seeing the lifeless body floating in the waves, hearing the phone call. 'Then they're all doing it,' I finished.

Gabriel's shoulder touched mine as he breathed. He smelled of woodsmoke and the fresh vegetabley smell of pumpkin insides. 'Does it help if I tell you that the main industry in Steepleton is fishing?' he asked.

I couldn't see his face; he'd got his head down, looking at

his hands where they rested along his thighs. 'I don't know what that means.'

A flick of a look. 'It means that most of the teenagers have lost someone to the sea. Maybe not their immediate family, maybe a grandparent or an uncle or a friend's dad. They all know how dangerous it is out there. There's not one of them that would get anywhere near the sea wall with the waves coming up over. People who play silly buggers, that's the tourists. The people from inland that think the sea is just for paddling and catching crabs on bits of string; they've never seen what it can really do.'

The rain splattered against the long window, and one of the bushes tapped the glass in a rising wind.

'But you can't promise she'll be safe,' I said, very very quietly.

He reached out and took my hand, it was so sudden it almost made me jump. 'Nobody can ever promise that,' he said and he still wasn't looking at me. 'Never. But it won't be any less safe than in here. She's fourteen and she needs independence.'

My throat clotted with all the reasons I couldn't let her do unsafe things, and I could practically hear the echo of Granny Mary in my head telling me to tell him, so that my control issues would look less bonkers. But I couldn't. I just couldn't.

'And you really don't need to take parenting advice from a guy who can barely see the end of his arms,' he said, his voice stronger and brighter now. 'Also, if I'm not mistaken, these pumpkins are not going to carve themselves, and it must be getting nearly time for the school bus drop-off.' He let go of my hand and went back to the pumpkins.

Almost as soon as he'd spoken I heard the unmistakable swish and rattle of the minibus coming down the lane. I hoped the crew had moved the caravan back into the orchard so that it could squeeze by.

'And it's... Thursday. End of half-term tomorrow, non-uniform day. So I predict...'

The front door flew open, its ancient brass handle ricocheting off the panelling in the hall, and Poppy blew inside, a whirlwind of books and bags and hair.

'Mum, it's non-uniform tomorrow, have you seen my Forever 21 jeans? And have you washed my white top?' Clomp clomp as the stairs were achieved, and then the voice drifting down. 'And I need my crop mesh Boohoo top, in case the white one isn't right, and my ASOS jacket to change into.'

'It's like living with a clothing catalogue,' I whispered to Gabriel. The clomping noises stopped.

'Mum? Who're you talking to? And where are you?'

'I'm in the living room,' I replied, thinking that the cottage had four rooms and a bathroom, I didn't really have a lot of choices. 'And Gabriel's here, helping out with the pumpkins.'

'Oh, *brill*!' The clomping came down the stairs again and Poppy flung herself into the room. 'Hey, Gabe.'

'Hi, Poppy. I'm just finishing this one off, might have to leave the other one until tomorrow. I ought to start back. Thea's got an order in for some crocheted stuff and we might have to work tonight to get it ready for despatch.'

Gabriel was back in front of the fire again as though he'd never been next to me, never taken my hand, but I could still feel the touch of his fingers echoing on my skin.

'You do crochet as well as the quilting?' I asked.

He looked up at me. There was a small half-smile on his face, almost as though he was reliving the feel of being next to me. 'Oh, yes. I am a positive list of manly attributes.'

'This is *amazing*!' Poppy had picked up the *Scream* pumpkin. 'So much better than Mum would have done!'

'Thanks, Pops,' I said, calmly.

'And I've finished my Cersei dress, and Rory says thanks for the help with his Jaime coat and the belt and stuff.'

'My pleasure.'

'And I'm going to stay over at Karen's next week, Mum, if that's okay, cos then I can work during the day and we can sort our costumes out after work and can you pick me up the day after the Halloween disco?'

'Oh, but I thought...' I started. Gabriel gave me a sideways look.

'Cos otherwise you'll have to drive me over there every morning in time for opening and it's really early and Karen's going to teach me how to bake the buns for the café and Rory's going to help me in the kitchen and I'm going to earn some money so that I can buy stuff to make some more costumes!' Poppy continued without a pause for breath. 'And Karen says would you like to come over to the café on Thursday for a coffee so you can see what a good job I'm doing, and you can bring my good boots over that I need for my costume.'

I opened my mouth to reply, but she carried on.

'Thanks, Mum. And thanks for the pumpkins, Gabe – what are you going to do with the second one? Can I have this one and you do one with zombies on for Rory?'

'Yes, but I shall have to finish it tomorrow, if your mum is okay with me coming back to do it? Or would you rather I took the other one down to Thea's and did it there?'

They were both looking at me. Poppy had the bright-eyed eager gleam that meant she was expecting results, and Gabriel was looking at me steadily. There was almost a touch of expectancy in his look too, now I thought about it, maybe linked to that brief moment we'd shared on the sofa.

'I...'

There was a banging at the back door that sounded as though someone was kicking a bucket, then a sudden gust of cold air. 'Is it all right if I fill the water up from your tap? Only Patrick needs a drink and I want to be able to put the kettle on first thing.'

We all jumped, as though the ghost of Mr Coombes had dragged itself into the living room.

'Of course, Mary,' I eventually called back, when my heart had settled down. 'Help yourself. Do you need a hand with the container?'

The scoff that came through was very audible. 'Don't be daft, girl. I've been hefting this thing about since before you could walk. Gabriel can help me.'

Poppy was about to speak, clearly to point out the contradictory nature of this statement, but Gabriel was getting to his feet and I shook my head at her. 'I'll come back to finish off that pumpkin, then, tomorrow?' He made it a question.

'Yes, of course, that would be nice.'

'I'll come and help you with Granny Mary's bucket,' and Poppy and Gabriel were gone, leaving me sitting in front of the spitting wood-burner. My heart was beating quickly, and at first I thought I was still reacting to the shock of Mary's calling through the house, but gradually I realised that it was the prospect of seeing Gabriel tomorrow.

I was actually looking forward to it. The feeling was so strange that I didn't recognise it, but there had been something in the way he'd taken my hand, something in the way he'd sat listening to me that had made me – what? Feel differently? Notice him as a man?

Then I shook my head. Nothing was going to happen with Gabriel. He was nice, but... we had the world's largest chaperone in the garden anyway.

Besides, Mary was right. If I wanted anything to happen between me and him, I'd have to tell him about my past, and I didn't want to do that.

I got up and straightened the cushions, drew the curtains across the darkening window. Stopped for a second in the middle of the room, which was now lit only by the flickering flames through the narrow glass pane in the stove door. From the kitchen I could hear Poppy giggling, carefree, happy. No expectations on her, other than making a decent attempt at her exams, no weight of a prospective future pulling her down.

I couldn't do it.

I left the room and closed the door firmly behind me.

12

Poppy left for school the next morning clutching bags of things she might need over the next week. I had to carry some of them to the bus stop for her, as her full rucksack kept giving way at the zip, although she wouldn't let me stay and wait for the bus with her.

'Mu-u-u-u-um, I'm *fourteen*! They'll think you've got, like, *issues* if you wait for the bus with me! I mean, durrr...' She made flapping motions with her hands. 'It's okay, I'll text you. And I'll see you on Thursday at the café anyway, and don't forget, it's the black boots with the heels, not the other ones, cos those would be stupid, they're somewhere in my room. Don't forget.' The flapping motions increased. 'Bus will be here in a minute. Mu-u-u-u-um!'

I gave in and went round the house to the front door. I didn't want to go in the back way in case Granny Mary was sitting outside the caravan waiting to give me the benefit of her experience or cadge some more biscuits.

Just before I went inside, I looked at Harvest Cottage. I rarely looked at it from the outside. It was invisible, hidden in its tiny lane that straggled off the main road, so you couldn't actually look at it from the outside unless you intended to. The off-centre chimney was extruding a scribble of smoke as I'd given in and lit the log-burner earlier that morning. I was telling myself that I did it to air the house out, whilst biting back the feeling that I was doing it to make the living room cosy for Gabriel's visit. The kitchen light was on and the living room door was open, so a muted gleam of light shone through and onto the soggy moss and bushes, making the pellets of rain that hung on each leaf glimmer, as though someone had dusted giant glitter over the garden.

The cottage looked inviting, and less wicked witch than it had done when we'd moved in. A bit more lived in. I'd stripped the door knocker of about a century of black paint and polished it, although, in deference to the film crew, I'd held off painting the front door so it still hung, slightly askew, flaking and dusty. But now when you went through, it gave onto a hallway where the floor was polished wood – thanks to hours on my knees with graded paper and wax – and it smelled of baking, of scented candles and polish, and not of rotting vegetation.

My house. Our *home*.

I went in, picking up the trail of destruction that Poppy always left on her way to school. A plate that had held toast was on the stairs, there was a mug of half-drunk tea two steps further down and her uniform, which needed washing, had been carefully disentangled from the rest of the detritus in her room and left sprawled between the bannisters and the kitchen doorway. Her tie was screwed up on the table. It lacked all the niceties of the London flat – the Grade A central heating, the double glazing that blocked the outside world, the designer furniture. But it felt more like home than that flat ever had done. Probably because the flat, our jobs, and Luc's insistence on maintaining the lifestyle he'd grown up with had meant a team of cleaners coming in every other day. The cottage just had me, and, on the other end of the scale, Poppy. No Gallic tutting, whenever he deigned to turn up, having been 'away' allegedly overseeing the family wine business or managing the estate, when he liked to complain about the 'mess', sweep Poppy off for a shopping expedition and expect me to put marking on hold to tidy up.

I felt a sudden rush of gladness that that was not my life any more.

Once the cottage was tidy, I went up and showered. I would not have admitted it to anyone, but I dressed a little more carefully than usual in black jeans that Poppy coveted and a slim knit sweater, and I even went as far as to apply a tiny amount of make-up for the first time since we'd come to Dorset. Only an almost invisible slick of lipstick, a dab of mascara and the merest hint of eyeliner, no more. I didn't want Gabriel to think I'd made an effort for him. Then I went back downstairs and put a batch of buns in the oven, so that the house smelled of fresh baking. I cut a few sprigs of mint from the pots on the window ledge and dotted them around the kitchen worktop in jam jars, for that *Good Housekeeping* touch, although the rather sparse nature of them actually looked more as though I was trying to keep moths at bay.

Then I sat down at the table and tried to work on the expression I'd be wearing when he turned up. Casual, relaxed, slightly surprised to see him – after all, hadn't I been so consumed by my hobby that I'd forgotten he was coming? I hastily put a book on the table and bent it open to look as though I'd been absorbed in reading. Then I realised that the book was Poppy's poetry textbook and shoved it into a corner.

I wanted to look spontaneous and relaxed, not as though I was planning an essay on Wordsworth. There was a half-read *Wuthering Heights* on the dresser and I replaced the poetry with that. Still a bit highbrow for off-the-cuff reading, but hopefully Gabriel wouldn't think I was taking Heathcliff as romantic inspiration.

I read a bit, then paced a bit. Got the buns out of the oven, redid my lipstick, then went upstairs to fetch my phone.

Gabriel had texted.

Sorry, the crochet is fighting back. Might not make it today, but I'll let you know.

Wuthering Heights hit the wall.

I changed out of the sexily cut jeans and the slim jumper, as neither of them were keeping me warm, and put on baggy cords, a chunky sweater and my boots. Then I filled up the spare bucket and went out to top up Patrick's water.

He was standing dozing at the far side of the orchard. His big piebald head came up when he saw me, but as I was evidently carrying nothing more interesting than water, it lowered again, and his fighting-crow ears twitched a greeting. I gave him a pat, ran a quick hand over his legs, which were so hairy that he looked as though he were wearing bootleg jeans, and could have had swellings from knee to fetlock but they'd have been invisible. Yesterday's toing and froing didn't seem to have done him any damage, other than exhaustion. He still had plenty of hay; his net was bulging from the tree, hanging damply in the unnaturally unmoving air. The forecasted storms were, so far, not evident. I breathed a sigh of relief. Maybe the weathermen had it wrong and Poppy's Halloween would be unruffled.

Then, reluctantly, I went up the steps to the van. I'd just lifted my hand to knock on the door, when the top half flew open.

'You not got any friends, then, eh?' Granny Mary poked her head out. 'You having to come calling on me for someone to talk to?'

'I was just going to ask if you'd like some tea,' I said, stiffly, because she was a little too close to the mark for my liking.

'I've got a kettle.' She pointed over her shoulder. 'Only thing I'm short of is biscuits.'

I took the hint and went back into the kitchen, returning to the van with the secret packet of Hobnobs that I'd had hidden in the back of the pantry.

'Come on in and have a cuppa.' Granny Mary had waited for me, her forearms on the door ledge, regarding the torpid orchard as though she were a fisherman on a seagoing vessel waiting for a whale to hove into view. 'Young Gabe not turned up yet, then?'

I went inside. It was dark in the van, with just the faint gleam from the fire in the stove illuminating it. Not much of the feeble October morning light was getting in through the small, high windows. It was warm and slightly fusty with the smell of shut-in wood. 'He's probably not coming, he's busy.' I tried to sound airy and as though I didn't care at all, but had to keep focused on the view of Patrick from the window, so she couldn't meet my eye.

'Oh ah. And here's you needing someone to talk to.' The kettle went on the hob. 'And wearing make-up.'

'I might go to Bridport. I came to see if you needed any shopping.' Patrick was scratching his tail against the mossy old tree, and it was simply *fascinating*. On the ground at his hooves, a blackbird pecked at the remains of the fallen apples, doing jumpy little hops to avoid being trodden on as Patrick wiggled his rump against the trunk.

'Hmmm.' Doubt dripped from the syllable.

I weakened. 'Yes, all right, I was hoping Gabriel would be coming, but it's complicated, Mary. You were right, I do need to talk to him about... about who I was, but it's—' I stopped. Couldn't put into words what it was. 'I don't think I can.'

'And, what? You think *I* should tell him? Save you the trouble?'

I had thought exactly that, but realised it would be a mistake almost as soon as I'd thought it. 'No. That wouldn't be fair.'

'Too right.' Mary poured the whistling kettle full of water into two mugs. Today she was resplendent in a NiN shirt with the logo 'Help Me, I Am In Hell'. It was disconcerting apparel on a little old lady pottering around in a caravan. 'If it doesn't come from you, it won't mean anything.' She pushed a mug towards me on the little table. 'Sit down. You're too big in here.'

I sat on the little bench that was fitted against the side of the van and tucked my legs under the tiny table, while Mary took up station on the other side, perched on a box. She took a sip of her tea and looked at me through the steam, without saying anything else. Her hair had grown out of its highlights whilst she'd been in the hospital, and a strange two-tone effect of grey was now mixed with the blonde and auburn streaks, making her look like a badger that had had a respray.

'She's a nice lass, your Poppy,' she said at last, reaching for another biscuit. 'You've done a good job there.'

'Thank you.'

'I don't think much of her father, mind. What were you

thinking? He carries on like he's still a teenager! A fancy accent will only take you so far, I told him that.'

I thought of Luc meeting Mary, and my lips twitched. He would have tried to charm her, but Mary was impervious to any charm that didn't come wrapped in silver foil and with a calorie content written in red.

'He's living with a twenty-six-year-old,' I said, 'and he's trying to keep up with her, I think.'

Mary scoffed. 'He's got to be forty if he's a day.'

'Forty-four, actually. He's ten years older than me.'

'And that was what you fell for, was it? Older man, swept you off your feet, gave you a reason not to go home?' Her mouth twisted. 'And then, whoops, you're pregnant, married, whole new life...' She stopped speaking suddenly and drank a large mouthful of tea.

I looked at her through the gloom. A little glimmer of realisation twinkled at the back of my mind. 'Who was he, Mary?' I asked, gently, but I was ready to duck in case she threw her mug at my head.

She sighed, but didn't reply.

We sat in the quiet for a while. I could hear the blackbird trilling in the bare branches and the squelch and rip that was Patrick grazing, but, apart from that, everything was still and calm. Mary was drinking her tea but looking down at the table; every so often she'd look up at the square of grey that was the window, and then back down again. She looked as though she was trying to make a decision.

Eventually she stood up. Without saying anything she went to the back of the van and rummaged around the bed area, then came back carrying something wrapped in a shawl. I really hoped it wasn't going to be a crystal ball.

With no flourish, in fact with a matter-of-fact air that was slightly belied by her hand shaking, she put the bundle down on the table. 'You're not as green as you're grass looking, are you?' she asked.

I presumed it was rhetorical and didn't reply.

Mary unwrapped the bundle. It was a framed photograph. Two women on what looked like a seaside promenade, windswept and arms linked. The older lady wore a fitted dress and a hat pinned onto swept back hair, the younger wore a smart blouse and skirt, her hair was long and blowing in the wind and she was laughing.

'Taken by one of those beach photographers that used to set up studios in seaside towns,' I observed, picking up the picture and tilting it to get some light on.

'Yes, this isn't a social history lesson, thank you,' Mary snapped. 'It was 1960. That girl is me.'

I looked again. Yes, I could see a foreshadowing of the Mary I knew in the face of that laughing girl, a curve of the chin and the mouth. In black and white I couldn't see the penetrating blue of her eyes, but beneath the laughter there was a hint of that direct gaze.

'And the other lady—' She stopped and took another mouthful of tea. 'That was my Rose.'

Rose was pretty in a stern, almost 1940s groomed way, and, although she was smiling too, there was an awkwardness about her. 'She doesn't look too happy about being photographed,' I observed.

'Yes. She was worried her husband might see us,' Mary said, almost as though she was daring me to pick up on this. 'He was my lecturer at university. She was the only person I ever found worth loving. And – well, clearly someone else had got there first.'

'Oh, Mary.' Suddenly so much of her prickliness made

sense.

'And if you're thinking that having had one brief love affair with a married woman way back when I was twenty-two scarred me for life and put me off ever falling in love again, then you are wrong, my girl.' She took the picture from my hands and wrapped it, almost tenderly, back in the scarf. 'And you also don't know much about human nature.' The picture was taken back to wherever it had come from, and carefully tucked away. 'People don't operate like that. Yes, she was married and things were different back then when you were... well, when you were like me. But I didn't give up on love on the strength of one doomed affair. I just never met anyone else.' She looked at me defiantly. 'It wasn't through want of trying, either. I've bonked my share. I just had a very busy job and – well, it never happened.'

'"Bonked"?' My voice sounded a bit feeble.

'Bonked, banged, shagged, screwed, whatever you call it these days. I can't keep up with the terminology, not really much point.' Mary sat back down again and picked up her mug. 'So, yes, there was someone, once. So, I do know what it's like. For your information.'

I pushed the biscuits across the table, closer to her hand.

'She was older than me. I wanted a reason to get away from home. I thought she'd leave her husband, run away with me, we'd have a little house on the clifftops and adopt a brood of children. I'd clearly read too many Charlotte Lamb novels. She liked her lifestyle and her successful husband too much.' Even in this half-light, the clear blue of her stare went right through me. 'So I do know a thing or two about using someone to escape from a situation.'

'Yes,' I said thoughtfully. 'I can see that.'

She got up and went to refill the kettle and I thought back

to my meeting Luc. His family had been distant friends of my mother's father, something to do with racehorses, so I'd been sent to stay with them after A levels, to improve my French. Why my mother thought a French degree was best for me, with my rather mixed bag of qualifications, I wasn't sure. Maybe she just thought it was a good way of shipping me off, out of her hair. Our relationship had been strained at best. We'd tried to keep out of each other's way, and she'd frequently left me whilst I'd been studying, travelling to Australia to stay with her sister for weeks at a time. Luc had been – well, he'd been older, handsome, interested. Before I knew it, I was pregnant, his mother was insisting on a wedding and...

'You won't be escaping too much with Gabe,' Mary said, eventually. 'Unless it's to an impeccably decorated house with really lovely soft furnishings.'

'I don't want to escape anything.' I put my mug down firmly. 'I like it here.'

'Well, then.' There was a tone of satisfaction in her voice, as though she'd just proved something. I wasn't sure what.

'But I still don't know if I can...'

Mary picked up my mug and sluiced it about in the bowl of water next to the stove. 'I just did it,' she said, with her back to me. 'Told you about Rosie. That wasn't easy either, even these days you can't be sure how people will take it, but, you see, it can be done.'

'But I have to think of Poppy. I can't move anyone in here, it's mine and hers, and she doesn't need a stepfather, she's got a perfectly good father of her own already. Even if he is a dick.'

'He's an expensively dressed dick, though, give him that.' Mary rinsed the mug and propped it, upside down, on the top of the stove. 'And nobody's saying that you should move Gabe in. He needs space, that boy, I've seen all the rubbish he generates. You can have a relationship these days without having to live together, you know.'

I opened my mouth to refute everything she'd said, then realised that it was actually quite sensible, and closed it again, then stood up. 'Well, thank you for the homilies, and general advice,' I said, as briskly as I could manage. 'I am sure my life will turn out for the best, without my needing a man in it. Now I have to go and polish something.'

Mary sighed and bent down to one of the painted cupboards. 'You might be right, you're better off without each other,' she said, straightening up with a bottle in her hand. 'If you can't tell him about your past, then let him go and find himself someone who'll be honest with him.'

'I didn't say...' But I trailed off. I had pretty much said exactly that.

'There's a couple of young lasses with that film crew who've got their eye on him,' Mary went on. 'And I don't reckon they've got this whole "complicated past" thing going on. His place up to Bridport is nice, they might want to shack up with him over there, eyesight or no eyesight.' She swung round. 'Here. Bottle of blackberry wine, made it myself last autumn.' The bottle, filled with a dark liquid that looked suspiciously thick, was thrust into my hands. 'His sister is absolutely bonkers, mind you, but she's a good girl. I'm sure they'll learn to cope with her. Now, you'd better go. I'm going to give Patrick a bit of a brush and then have a nap.'

I took the bottle and went out into the daylight, which, even though it was slightly muted and sunlight-free, seemed almost overwhelmingly bright after the darkness of the caravan interior.

* * *

Gabriel didn't make it over for several days. He texted, apologising and hoping that the pumpkins would keep, but he had to finish a quilt that was on express order.

I went to Bridport and spent more in the supermarket than I had intended. I also went to the big DIY warehouse and bought paint, and started painting the kitchen, to the evident consternation of the resident woodlice.

Outside the weather forecasters were being proved right by the gusty storms that were passing through the county. There was so much rain that the ford at the bottom of our lane had become impassable and access to the other side of the valley had to be via a five-mile detour down the main road. I'd stomped down to stare moodily into the swirling brown waters and texted Poppy some pictures of the depth gauge, which said that the water was 1.5 metres deep. She texted me back a 'LOL', I wasn't quite sure why, but apparently she was working hard in the café, it was busy, and her evenings were spent being taught to bake by Karen.

I had a little shiver of resentment towards Karen. *I* should have been teaching Poppy to bake! And then I got real and remembered that Poppy had been utterly dismissive whenever I'd tried to entice her into the kitchen to learn any life skills, and had informed me that she'd just ring out for a pizza when she left home and didn't need to learn to cook. Karen was clearly having more luck than me, or perhaps it was cooler to learn these things when it wasn't your mother teaching you.

So, on the Wednesday morning, when Gabriel finally turned up, of course I was wearing paint-stained jeans and hoodie and had just got back from giving the ford another good staring at. Which meant that my hair was soaked and plastered to my head and my skin had that strange tight feeling from being subjected to a high wind all the way back up the lane. I must have looked like a Botoxed seal.

'Hello,' Gabriel said cheerfully, as I wrenched open the front door with a towel over my head. 'I've come to finish the pumpkins for Friday. I know you're going down there tomorrow, and I rushed the quilt through so I could come over and get the carving done in time for you to take them down. Why have you got a towel on your head?'

I thought slightly longingly about the slim-fit jeans and the silky sweater that I'd planned to wear for him, and the subtle make-up. The crotch of the jeans I was wearing was somewhere round my knees and the hoodie was so large that it was only a couple of guy ropes short of being a tent.

'I was outside,' I said, through towelling. 'I wasn't expecting you.'

'You look like a rapper sponsored by Farrow & Ball.' He looked me up and down again. 'Nice colour, by the way. Where's it going?'

'Mostly up my legs.' I led the way into the hall and he followed me. 'And the rest is on the kitchen walls. It's been okay'd by Keenan, before you panic.'

I hadn't bothered to light the stove or the wood-burner, and the inside of the cottage had the patina of damp again. It did, however, smell a bit nicer since I'd discovered Bridport had a lovely scented-candle shop. I'd decided the artistic sprigs of mint made it smell like a chewing-gum factory and thrown them away.

'Sorry I didn't text or ring to say I was coming,' Gabriel looked at the painting detritus spread over the flags. 'I wasn't completely sure myself until Thea said she'd take the quilt off to post. Then I thought I'd just take my chances.' He held up a bag. 'I've brought my pumpkin-carving kit. You know, because I value my fingers and your knives might be great for hacking and slashing at unwanted visitors, but – actually, now I realise I might be an unwanted visitor and should *not* have pointed that out.'

That made me laugh. 'Of course, you're not unwanted.'

He gave me a grin. His hair was all dishevelled by the wind, tangled around his head and caught in the graze of stubble up his cheeks. It made him look slightly exotic. 'Good. Because I've also brought a party.' He held up the rucksack that he'd evidently peeled off his back.

'I'm sorry?'

'You were right. Why *should* the kids have all the fun? I know it's not Halloween until Friday, but I just thought, well, we can test out the pumpkins, and I brought some WKD and some crisps...' He dug in the bag and pulled out the items. Four bottles of luridly blue WKD, and two tubes of crisps. 'And also a CD of "Songs of the Nineties", which I reckon will do us both as music.'

I stared at him, slowly rubbing the towel over my hair to make it look as though I was doing something rather than thinking fast. He'd remembered. That throwaway remark I'd made about Halloween parties – *he'd remembered*. 'Wow.'

'Well, yes, obviously, it's not *much* of a party, but I grew up in Steepleton. Three people, one of whom knew all the words to "Livin' la Vida Loca", and a packet of Quavers, and you'd got a party. Alcohol and Pringles makes this practically an invitation-only ball.'

I was still staring at him from underneath the towel. 'You're wet,' I said, eventually.

'Oh. Oh.' He sat down on the nearest kitchen chair, one of

the serial killer ones that Kee had left – they really were going to have to go. Onto the wood-burner, for preference, although since my better ones were now stacked in the shed and probably covered in cobwebs, I didn't have a lot of choice other than to keep using them for now. 'Yes. Sorry. Um. Yes. Look, I'll go back and take the pumpkins with me. I can give them to Rory on Friday.' He stood up again, the legs of the chair making a horrible noise on the flagstones. 'Sorry. Again.'

'*What?*' I pulled the towel off my head. 'What the hell are you on about?' Why the hell was he talking about leaving when he'd only just arrived? *And* had brought alcohol?

'You said...' Realisation slowly dawned, his eyes widened behind the glasses and he looked down at himself. His coat was dripping on the floor. 'Oh. You meant *literally* wet.'

'Of course, I did! You didn't think I meant...' I stared at him. 'You thought I was calling you pathetic? Gabriel...' I didn't know how to finish that sentence. He was still looking at the floor.

'It scars you, you know.' His voice was very quiet. 'If they'd attacked me with razor blades or something, you'd see the marks. But they attacked me with words, and that's worse, because people forget words. They forget what they said and how they were, and you're supposed to smile and say that we're all grown up now and it's done and forgotten, but it fucking *isn't*.' He flicked a glance up to my face. I don't know what expression he saw there but he carried on talking. 'If I had scars all over my arms I could hold them up and say, "This is what you did to me." But there's nothing to see. So I have to pretend it's all right, but it lives on inside you like some kind of little fireworm that flares up every now and again and just eats away at the person you've tried so hard to be.'

I put a hand on his arm. Now he looked in my face, properly, scanning me, and I didn't know what he could see, or how much of what I felt was showing. 'Bullying is *wrong*.' They were all the words that came to me.

'Look, I'm sorry I reacted like that. It's actually becoming increasingly obvious what you really meant – it's soaked through to my underwear – and I'm sorry I got a bit...' He tailed off. His eyes were huge. 'Yeah,' he finished.

I wanted to move in closer. To give him a hug, to push my hands through that hair that the wind had already had a good go at. But I didn't want him to think I was pitying him, or that the fact he'd been bullied made him somehow 'lesser' in my eyes. So I did what I did when Poppy started to lapse into self-analysis when I just didn't have the time – I went practical.

'Right, you'd better get your coat off, then. We can put it in the living room and I'll light the fire. I'll get the stove going in here too, and you should dry out quite quickly. You might steam a bit, mind.' I gave him an upbeat grin. 'The other pumpkin is still in front of the log-burner. It might be getting a bit wrinkly but it should still be fine, and if we sit in there it will be warmer.' I picked up his rucksack. 'And crisps? As Pink so memorably said, let's get this party started!'

I just wanted to wipe that look off his face. That look that said he knew that he'd been friend-zoned, but I couldn't. I didn't dare. To be anything more to Gabriel meant, as Mary repeatedly pointed out, opening myself up, and I couldn't do that. So was it better for him to think that I really did consider that doing crochet and making those beautiful quilts made him somehow not quite a real man in my eyes?

Oh, shit, this was complicated.

As he gathered up his materials and moved through into the other room, I glanced out of the back window, into the orchard. Patrick was over the far side, chewing something in the hedge with a thoughtful expression and his ears cocked sideways. Granny Mary was standing on the steps of the van, looking right at me. I knew, absolutely *knew* that she hadn't been able to hear any of that conversation between Gabriel and me, yet there was something very *knowing* about that direct blue stare. As though she was somehow telling me that it was time to make up my mind.

Okay. Okay, I could do this.

13

Darkness pulled tight against the walls of the cottage, but we hardly noticed, because inside we'd lit all the candles and were singing 'Mambo No. 5' at the tops of our voices. The WKD was gone, as were the crisps, and we were halfway through Granny Mary's blackberry wine and some posh cheese that I'd bought to eat in my solitude while Poppy was away and couldn't complain about the smell.

'This is *great!*' I said, twirling around to Backstreet Boys, which meant that my hoodie and I parted company for a while until it caught up with me again and wrapped itself around me like a mummy's bandages. 'You were right, Gabe! The kids shouldn't have all the fun!' I took another swig of the wine. It tasted like a cross between fruit cordial and cough mixture and was going down a treat. I was doing that dance that involves holding one arm up in the air, punching to the rhythm, whilst jiggling about with my head down. I'd tried twerking but had fallen over and we'd laughed so much I'd worried I'd be sick.

'Yeah.' He'd taken his coat and jumper off, and was

dancing in his shirt and chinos, although his dancing was more in the nature of rotating both shoulders and wriggling his hips, like Elvis doing the Locomotion. He refilled his glass.

We'd lit both pumpkin lanterns and they, and the glowing logs in the stove, provided the only light, which meant I kept tripping over things, and eventually I fell over the ancient CD player, causing Destiny's Child to stammer over 'Independent Women' and skip straight into Dido. Gabriel reached out a hand and pulled me back up.

'You can't dance down there.'

I stayed where his rescue landed me, pulled up close against him. The blackberry wine made my arms go very heavy and I put them around him so I could rest them. His arms came up and around me and suddenly I was much, much closer to him than I had been, feeling his warmth through his shirt and his breath on my forehead. I rolled my face upwards so that I could see him.

'This is nice.'

'Yes, you are.' His voice was very quiet, and I felt the words rise up through his chest rather than hearing them. He was looking down at me now, glasses making his eyes huge and the low-level lighting making them very dark. The reflections of twin pumpkin lanterns burned in both pupils, like looking into tiny inviting hells. 'You are lovely.'

And then I was stretching forward and upwards against the length of him, and he was leaning downwards and our mouths met in the middle, all fire and blackberries, and his mouth was warm and tasted of the autumn. Also, slightly, of crisps.

We drew apart and Dido sang sadly about her lover leaving. I put my head against Gabriel's chest and we danced together circling in the glow from *Scream* and *The Walking Dead* as they threw spooky shadows into the room and the logs crumpled into ash in the wood-burner. Dido stopped singing, and nobody took her place, but still Gabriel and I circled, arms around one another, my head in the crook of his neck and his chin resting on the top of my head. It felt good. It felt right.

Eventually we stopped and just stood. I looked up at him, his eyes black in the candlelight. 'I need to tell you something,' I said. 'But I can't.'

I felt him inhale. One deep breath against me. 'Then don't,' he said.

'It's not fair if I don't.' My wine was still at the end of my arm. That surprised me. I'd been holding the glass between Gabriel's shoulder blades, but he'd put his down to rescue me from Destiny's Child.

He went very still, almost as though he'd stopped breathing, and there was a very faint tightening of his hold. 'Please,' he whispered. 'Please, just let's have this.'

There was a pause. Just enough time for the world's heart to beat once, as I lingered there in his arms, wishing I could forget, let it go. But Granny Mary, damn her, had been right: I *had* to tell him. Although he was right too, and we could just have this...

I took half a step back so I could bring my arm round to drink, and he didn't let go of me. He smelled of the blackberries in the wine, and of clean washing and the outdoors. 'You smell nice.'

'So do you.' He put his cheek against my hair. 'Sort of fruity.'

'Might be the wine. Might be Poppy's *really* expensive perfume that her dad buys her and I borrow when she's not around.' I took another breath. 'Mmm. Nice. Not that I'm sniffing you or anything.'

'I wouldn't mind if you were.'

'But I can't... I can't... you and I, we can't... because I can't, and it wouldn't be fair.'

'Okay, coherence has gone. What *is* this stuff anyway?' He intercepted my hand and drank some of the wine from my glass. 'Have you been using it to strip paint?'

'Granny Mary.' For some reason my eyelids felt really, really heavy as well as my arms now. I closed them. It was fine. His chest was taking the weight of my head, because that felt heavy too.

'Oh dear.'

'Why? Wassup?' I tried to look up into his face, but could only see the bottom of his chin. 'You're very tall. Why you so tall?'

'Granny Mary's wine is leggy... legundo... ledgery. Dangerous stuff.' His voice was slow. 'We should blow the candles out. Before we. Before. Thing.' He let go of me equally slowly, sort of unwinding himself from around me, and bent down. His glasses fell off. ''S not safe.'

A few ineffectual puffs and a lot of giggling and we managed to blow out the candles, which put the room in near total darkness. Only the red glow of the fire illuminated a small patch of the carpet and the sofa, which suddenly seemed very attractive.

'Let's sit down,' I said.

* * *

The next thing I knew was a steely cold stream of water running down the outside of the windows. I watched it for a while, dispassionately, wondering why I was so warm underneath and cold on top and how it had got light so quickly. My eyes felt a bit sticky, so I blinked hard once or twice, then tried to rub my face, but couldn't.

'I think I'm paralysed,' I said.

And then jumped when a voice underneath me said, 'That's because I'm lying on your hand.' Slowly I turned my head. It chafed against a half-buttoned shirt and the velvet of the sofa, and ended up staring into Gabriel's face, where he lay underneath me, without his glasses but with a big soot mark down one cheek. His eyes were closed. 'If I open my eyes, am I going to regret it?'

I did a quick mental inventory. I was fully dressed, but minus the hoodie, probably why I felt cold. Apart from the stickiness of my eyes, there was no abnormal feeling around my face, no stubble burn or dribble or anything. 'What the hell happened?'

'At a guess, Granny Mary's wine. I am going to *kill* her.' He still hadn't opened his eyes. 'Eventually. Although I have to say I'm going to take my time, because this actually feels rather nice.' A cautious arm came up around my back.

I could feel his ribs and one hip pressing into me. At least, I *hoped* it was his hip. 'Urgh. Did we...?'

'I think we just passed out.' One eye opened cautiously. 'I don't *think* anything else happened and I'd like to think that's the sort of thing I'd remember.'

He was so warm. And the arm was around me, not pulling me in but just balancing me. This close up I could see the stubble that highlighted his jaw and his eyelashes flickering against his cheekbone like stop frame animation. 'Gabriel, I need to tell you.'

A finger came up and covered my mouth. 'No. No, you don't.'

'I think I want to, though.' I couldn't explain it. Maybe it was the way he was lying there, unhurried and relaxed underneath me, his hand gently stroking my shoulder. Maybe it was just the way he was, damaged and yet not allowing that damage to define him. Maybe it was just the sheer volume of wine we'd drunk. But I actually wanted to tell him.

Rain hit the window as though it had been fired from a cannon and splattered into the silence.

'My name was Katherine Bryant,' I said. The name that had once been so familiar now tasted like a strange food. 'My father was Alexander Bryant.' Then I stopped. I could feel Gabriel's breathing underneath me.

'I vaguely know the name,' he said. 'But I can't...'

'Gold medal. Equestrian. Well, two gold medals, an individual and a team gold. He was a three-day eventer.'

I could almost see Dad's face, strong and smiling, hair wet where he'd taken his skull cap off after the final showjumping round, slapping at his horse's neck as he slid to earth to greet me with wide arms. 'We did it, Katie! Boomer and me, we did it!'

'Mum worked the youngsters – we had a yard full of horses. Dad had sponsors and owners queueing up. It all was great, very successful. But—' I had to stop.

'You rode?' Gabriel's voice was quiet. The arm around my back had stopped moving.

'My mum...' Oh, God, how did I put it? How could I frame the words so they encompassed my growing up? 'She was very keen for me to event. Put me in a saddle before I could walk, sent me off around the practice course Dad had built at home when I was ten, on one of the older horses. I was *terrified*, but I couldn't tell her. She wanted me to succeed, wanted me to take over some of Dad's rides; I kept trying to explain that I didn't – never mind.'

I took a deep breath and pushed myself up to sitting, clear of him now. 'When I was fourteen, Dad and I were out exercising. I was riding a young horse, Kelso – we called him Kelly.' I half smiled, a memory of the warm stable and a greeting whicker over the buckets, a big bay gelding with a head like a racehorse and a back like a whale. 'Dad was riding his medal horse, Boomer; we were out on the road getting ready to turn into the gallops. Kelly started being nappy, trying to whip round, so Dad and I swapped over. He had stronger legs than me and he could get any horse to do anything...' I swallowed hard. The images were still there. They lurked like dark things in the depths of a lake, circling beneath the surface, waiting to be called.

'A car came round the bend, too fast. Boomer ran up into the hedge, but the car hit Kelly full on.' Yes, there it was, the sound that haunted my dreams: the dull noise of impact and a horse screaming. 'Dad was killed outright. Kelly... the vet came and...' I swallowed again. 'It was my fault. If we hadn't swapped horses, Dad would still be here. It was my fault. If I'd just been a better rider it wouldn't have happened. And my mother made sure I knew that. We lost the yard. Mum couldn't keep it going on her own and she, well, she never really got over any of it. We moved to London, gave up horses and things were never the same again.'

Gabriel was sitting up now, next to me. His face looked oddly naked without his glasses and he was looking down at his knees so I couldn't see his eyes. 'Fourteen,' he said, almost wonderingly. 'You were only fourteen.'

'My mother never let me forget that it should have been me.' And here was the widening of my throat that paradoxically stopped the words from coming and I had to swallow hard and screw up my eyes. 'We shouldn't have swapped horses, and it should have been me that got hit on Kelly.'

Gabriel made a noise like someone startled, a sharp indrawing of breath. 'Your mother said that? To *you*?'

'She was upset and angry. We'd had to sell up and move and give the horses back to their owners and it was all because of me. And I'd had everything, she'd given up everything to try to turn me into an eventer as good as my dad, and it had all gone, in that one afternoon. Because I wasn't a good enough rider to stop a horse from trying to turn for home.' A couple of tears escaped from my rigid control. 'I loved my dad, but I didn't want to do what he did. I was never good enough, not strong enough or driven enough. I was a decent rider but I didn't care about being successful – that was all Mum. She'd always wanted to be an event rider, but she had a weak back, she couldn't ride the big fences and—' I stopped. 'I loved my dad,' I said again, my voice trailing into a pitiful little sob that made me hate myself just a little bit more. 'And you had to know, Gabriel.'

In one swift movement he put his arms around me and held me in the new silence that was broken only by the rain weeping down the glass.

I didn't cry. I'd cried myself to a standstill all those years ago, unheard. My mother had been too deep in her own grief to console me, and there hadn't been anyone else. The stable girls had all had to be let go. I remembered several of them crying at leaving their favourite horses, and I'd hidden my grief by crying in sympathy with them. Now there were no tears left. So I rested my forehead against Gabriel's shoulder and let him take the weight of my sorrow.

The wind rattled the windows and the smell of charred wood puffed out of the now-cold log-burner as the breeze came down the chimney.

'I have to go over to Warram today,' I said, my voice slightly muffled by Gabriel. 'I'm seeing Karen and taking Poppy her boots.' The prosaic nature of the forthcoming day was good; it quietened me. Kept me nailed to the here and now and from sliding back into those days of grief and loss or, even worse, the time before. Dad, always cheerful and upbeat, training hard, and Mum – well. Always on my back about something: how I didn't need to study, I needed to ride. I should be working on my strength, on my endurance, on dealing with the more difficult horses instead of riding the steady workers. I should be in the manège, getting a good collected trot, a round outline, a good balance.

'Great. We can take the pumpkins too.'

But he kept hold of me. Somehow the feel of his warm body and the regularity of his breathing was reassuring. There was a steadiness to Gabriel, I realised. Not the escapist 'money solves everything' of Luc, but a more grounded feel.

'Do you think I'll be legal to drive? That wine was awfully, um, effective.'

He laughed and the rock of his shoulder under my cheek made me smile. 'I've always suspected Mary of putting something extra in her wine. Don't know what it is, but it's had some very odd effects over the years.'

Gradually, cautiously, we unwound ourselves as though

we were embarrassed. I didn't know what to say. The kiss, that had been something, but it could have meant nothing. Me telling Gabriel, well, it moved us on to another level, whether he knew it or not, and I didn't know where we went from here. Apart from over to Warram, armed with two carved pumpkins and a pair of high-heeled boots.

14

We drove down to Warram Bay, against the wind, with my car working hard, rocking at every gateway we passed. Cars were being diverted along the road, away from the coast, everyone driving cautiously in vehicles that were as prone to shying across the road as skittish horses. The wind boomed and crashed through empty trees and telephone wires and when we reached the clifftop we could hear the surf being forced high onto the beaches and rocks.

Gabriel seemed unconcerned. 'We get storms every autumn,' he said, cleaning his glasses on the sleeve of his coat. 'They go through right into winter. It's why we always tell tourists to spend a whole year here before they buy their "perfect houses". Dorset is a very different place out of summer.'

He was carefully not looking at me directly, although I could sense little covert glances now and then from the passenger seat. He'd got the two pumpkin lanterns balanced on his knees, the carvings looking just like random slashes now they were unilluminated. I took a few covert looks of my own at his capable hands, cupping the fruit carefully. Long, artistic fingers, Sensitive hands. A sensitive man.

'I shouldn't have told you,' I said suddenly, fighting to hold the line as the car was buffeted by a gust where hedges ended. 'I'm sorry. I didn't mean to put all that on you.'

He turned his head as though he was looking out of the window. Since I knew he could barely see past the end of his nose I knew he was trying not to let me see his expression. 'I'm glad you did. It explains a lot.'

'Me being a bit overprotective of Poppy? Yes, I know. It's just hard, she's exactly the age I was when... well, when it all happened.' I took a deep breath. 'I can't bear to think of her having even one-tenth of the feelings I had when I was fourteen. It *should* be all pop bands and arguments about shoes and staying out late, not—' I stopped. *Not crying in the night, hearing the horses being loaded and taken away. Not the way my mother looked at me, with a quiet, resigned contempt. Not moving from the big farmhouse with the dogs and the acres of space to a London flat, sealed against noise and weather.* It struck me then that we'd done almost the literal opposite. I'd moved Poppy from her centrally heated flat-dwelling life to this open wildness. Was I trying to undo what had been done to me?

'I mean, it explains why you seem to understand. About the bullying.'

I had to concentrate to steer the car though heaps of windblown detritus on the road. 'I don't understand,' I said, weaving us in and out of large lumps of branch from the hedge and hoping not to catch a tyre.

'You were bullied too, just in a different way. Mine was being picked on for being different, yours was being *pushed* into being different. You didn't want to be an eventer but your mum thought you should be and so she – well, bullying takes all kinds of forms, doesn't it? It's not all being shoved into swimming pools. It can be insidious and it can come from the people who are meant to love you.'

I turned the car down the narrow track that led to Warram Bay, without replying, although I'd got a little weevil of acknowledgement making its way into my heart. I'd often thought that I let Luc bully me; when we were married he'd practically dictated the terms of our marriage. He'd be allowed to come and go as he pleased but I had to stay at home and look after Poppy, bring up our daughter in the way he saw fit. Even now we were no longer together he still turned up when he felt like it and expected to be welcomed and fêted. But then, the amount of money he spent on Pops when he did visit bought him a fair bit of welcome and fêting.

I'd never thought of my mother as a bully. I'd thought of her as someone who wanted me to have something that she had never had – a career in eventing. But now I came to think of it, those subtle digs about me spending time doing other things, practically *anything* other than riding, those had all been geared towards making me change my behaviour, hadn't they? Those hints that she'd be disappointed if I didn't do as she said and the quiet withdrawal of affection when I didn't fall in with her plans? Weren't they just bullying by the back door? 'I don't feel like she bullied me,' I said quietly. 'I could always have said no.'

Now Gabriel looked directly at me, blinking those big dark eyes behind his glasses. One hand let go of the pumpkin and reached across to touch mine on the steering wheel. 'And what about after your father died?' The question was very quiet. 'What about when she realised that you weren't going to live her ambitions for her? What then?'

The wind squealed past us. We were heading down the

steep slope towards the café and I could see the waves hurling themselves up onto the beach in great grey curls of foam and angry water. 'She was upset,' I said flatly. 'The things she said – I know it wasn't really *her*. She'd lost her husband and we'd had to move.'

'But she took it out on you. Made it your fault. That's bullying too, Katie. And it was *never* your fault – how could it have been?'

'If I'd been better. If we hadn't switched horses...'

'If you hadn't then the car might have swerved and still hit your dad. His horse might have behaved differently with him and not run into the hedge. It was an accident, that was all, and she had no right to make you a scapegoat to save her facing up to that fact.'

We reached the car park outside the café. There was only one other car there; this wasn't the weather for holidaymakers to be walking the beaches. Spray was being thrown far enough to be splattering down off the café roof, mingling with the occasional rain and peppering the car park with gobbets of weed. The sparse grasses that grew up the dunes were bent double under the wind, and the sands were shifting.

'Gabriel.' I stopped the car and we sat as the engine ticked into quiet, backed by the booming roar of the waves. 'I know it wasn't my fault. I know it was an accident. I suspect my mother knows that too, but it's gone too far for both of us now. All I can do is try to protect Poppy from ever feeling the way I did when I was her age. If it sometimes makes me a controlling mother, then that's the price I pay for making sure she knows I love her.'

'And it's why you're nervous of Patrick?'

His eyes moved over my face. They kept coming back to my mouth, which was distracting.

'I'm not nervous of him, as such. I just know how unpredictable horses can be. Kelly had never ever tried to whip round on me before, never shown any signs of being nappy. He was a gentle soul, young and green but coming on really well, and I don't know what he saw in the hedge that day that made him shy but... anyway. I don't want Poppy anywhere near horses. They aren't safe.'

'Safe.' He moved in his seat so he was closer to me. 'Katie, *nothing* is ever completely safe. Even my sewing machine has been through my hand a few times. I've poked myself in the eye with my sodding *glasses* and they're blunt and plastic and only one step away from remedial cutlery.' He touched my cheek, his fingers gently stroking along the plane of my face until he cupped my chin. 'Nothing is safe,' he repeated. 'And you need to remember that.'

I was leaning in, as though he were magnetic and I was some kind of bendy metal. My lower half stayed put behind the wheel but my top half was pulled towards him, in his big black coat, until his hand moved to the back of my head and he was kissing me. His lips were firm, his mouth was hot and there was toothpaste and wine and something else that tasted rich and dark like a secret promise on the edges of that kiss.

When we broke apart I just sat and looked at him for a moment. 'Is that a warning?'

He frowned. 'No, that was a kiss. Understandable confusion there, but warnings usually come with sirens or klaxons or something.'

'I meant you saying that nothing was safe. Are you oh-so-subtly trying to tell me that you aren't safe?'

The car rocked in the wind and the wiper blades howled. Gabriel blinked once or twice. 'Katie,' he said slowly, 'in five, ten, years, I could be unable to see much more than to tell light from dark. So, no, if you're looking for a man who'll sweep you off your feet and carry you to Monaco for a weekend of rampaging and sightseeing, then, no. I'm not safe.'

Cautiously I put up a hand and brushed some of his unruly hair away from his face. 'What if that's not what I want?' I asked quietly.

'If you want a man who will always try to put you first and who is, quite frankly, besotted with you to an almost lunatic degree, then I'm as safe as houses.' His voice was quiet and had the tone of one who expects to be slapped down.

There was a pause, during which the car rocked a bit more.

'And whilst I am trying not to draw conclusions from the ongoing silence, I am afraid that conclusions are very much being reached. I'm sorry, I shall keep my emotional tendencies in check from now on.'

'Gabriel...' I couldn't think of anything to follow up with. My heart was scudding against my ribcage as though I'd swallowed a Viking longship and the oars were still going. 'My life is... complicated.'

'And mine is so totally straightforward that I've got my pension predicted to the last penny? Nobody *ever* knows. Not ever. My sight may stay as it is. It might go completely. I've learned that complicated is just another word for "life".'

I glanced quickly over at the doorway to the café. Karen had obviously heard the car pull up and our lack of appearance in the café had made her concerned enough to come and peer out into the car park. The wind made her hair do a 360-degree arc around her head and her apron attempted to escape.

'I mean, it's complicated, as in I can't just say, "Oh, yes, let's have a relationship," and move you into the cottage. I have Poppy to think about, and even though she's taken my divorcing her father reasonably well I'm not going to subject her to a series of uncles.'

His lips twitched. 'Firstly, I wouldn't expect you to. I have a perfectly good house of my own and no desire to share a bathroom with a teenage girl any more often than was strictly essential. Secondly, I don't intend to be one of a series and I'd hope you'd see me more as an endpoint than a starting block. Thirdly, Poppy always has to come first in anything we may do. I'm sure there's a fourthly, but it's not springing immediately to mind. But I am otherwise encouraged by the fact that you haven't instantly recoiled. Or told me that I'm lovely but you see me as a friend.'

I looked at him sitting there, dark and with those incredible cheekbones. His face was so familiar now that noticing his good looks startled me afresh every time. 'I'd like... no. Not as a friend,' I said, and my voice was thick with a sort of desire. 'It's more than that.'

'Excellent!' He gave me a cheerful grin and opened the car door. 'Now, let's seal our pact with Karen's excellent buns. Good Lord, that sounded really skeevy, didn't it? Sorry.'

The wind took the car doors and flung them wide, then stirred all the detritus that naturally came to rest in the car into demonic motion. Every sweet wrapper in the world arose and sought its revenge, whirling around as though trying to manifest in earthly form. We slammed the doors and I watched it all come to rest again. My heart felt a lot like the car interior right now, only with less Werther's Original packets. It was whirling and dancing around in my chest, stirred into unfamiliar motion by his declaration and the implications. Gabriel took my hand and we ran across the car park like two children dashing into school, heads ducked to reduce us as targets for the water splatters and the wind.

The inside of the café was a huge contrast to the outside. Warm and still, the only real noise some gentle background conversation and the tinkle of fork against plate. It was a little bit like coming across Miss Marple during the apocalypse.

'Hey, glad you made it over!' Karen bore down on us, apron rustling. 'Turning a bit wild out there now, typical autumn. How are you, Gabe?'

'Improving daily, Kaz, thanks.' Gabriel still had hold of my hand and he gave my fingers a squeeze. 'Life is continuing to surprise me.'

'Sit down over there. I'll go get you some muffins. Poppy made 'em this morning, thought you might want to see how they turned out. She'm a little gem in the kitchen, that one.'

We sat down at a table by the window. I felt an odd kind of torn pride: on the one hand my daughter was baking edible goods and clearly working hard at learning a new skill, but on the other hand – did it have to be waitressing and working in a kitchen? I looked up and caught sight of Poppy and Rory. She was piling a new load of buns under a glass dome, hair up and neatly uniformed, while Rory was wiping down a table on the far side of the café. They both looked content and I gave myself a talking-to. Okay, working in a kitchen wasn't my idea of high achievement, but I absolutely was *not* going to turn into my mother and dictate to Pops what she should and shouldn't do with her life. If she wanted to spend it turning out baked goods and wiping down woodwork, well, so be it. I'd just have to learn to deal with that.

Poppy looked up and saw us, then gave me a little wave. She called something over her shoulder to Rory, who looked over as well and smiled. Smiling did things to his face that showed what he'd look like in another few years, given a growth of stubble and a less bonkers haircut; he had a strong jawline and intelligent dark eyes and once he grew into his body he'd be a decent-looking lad.

I waved back.

Karen came over with coffees and settled herself into a chair. Gabriel got up.

'I'm going to give Rory the pumpkins,' he said. 'And let you two talk. Don't worry, Kaz, I'll grab a bite and a coffee with the kids.' And he sauntered off across the café, one pumpkin in each hand, like an ambidextrous spin bowler.

'Hm, tact from our Gabe. He must be growin' up.' Karen's eyes followed him across the wood-panelled interior. 'He's turned into a real looker, that boy.'

'Mmm,' I said, not wanting to incriminate myself.

Karen raised an eyebrow at me. 'And you aren't fooling nobody,' she said, slightly tartly. 'Just you watch out with that one – his heart is near the surface and a bit fragile.'

The incongruity of getting the mother-in-law talk from a woman my age made me suppress a little giggle. 'It's very early days for us, Karen,' I said, trying to sound neutral. 'We're just feeling our way.'

'Don't you go feeling his way in those trousers.' Karen glanced over at Gabriel, who was showing the pumpkins to an animated Poppy and Rory. 'He'll get arrested.'

We both gave a conspiratorial giggle. I absolutely wasn't going to ask how much of Gabriel she had personally felt; no doubt that would come up in conversation at some point, but I wasn't sure now was the time. 'How's Poppy been getting on?' I sipped at the coffee.

'Like I said, she'm a gem. Talking about going to catering college or summat when she leaves school.' Karen gave me a small smile as though she'd read my thoughts. 'I'm tryin' to talk her out of it. She's too good for this place. Rory says she's gettin' really friendly with that Sharon as does the costumes on set for *Spindrift*, as was helping them turn out their frocks for the do tomorrow. *He* says Sharon says that your Poppy has an eye for costume – make of that what you will.' A quick look over at where Poppy had brought out something in a bag and was showing it to Gabriel; a swatch of scarlet fabric told me it was probably the dress that Gabriel had helped with. 'Between him and her, you could find yourself up to your ears in hems and selvedge, whatever that is.'

I sipped again at my coffee. Karen was watching me from under hair that still hadn't quite settled after the wind. She seemed to want to say something else but not to know how to go about it, and, as Karen seemed set to put 'forthright' on the map, I thought it must be something I didn't really want to hear. She twisted her mouth around the rim of her cup, taking little jabbing sips like one of those drinking-bird toys.

Over at the counter Rory and Poppy whooped with laughter at something Gabriel said. I looked over and caught his eye for a moment. His face was relaxed and I thought how different he looked when he was happy. Less like a manga hero, all square and straight lines, more like something that had been borne in on the wind, a force of nature. He winked and I had to hide a rising blush inside my mug.

'Your ex-husband came in yesterday,' Karen said at last. 'Had a bit of a barney with your Poppy over working here rather than going to visit her... grommar?'

'Grand-mère,' I said. 'Luc's mother can be rather *forceful*. She's probably put the pressure on him to get Poppy to visit.' A sudden memory of Luc and his need to defer to his mother in everything, probably the only reason we'd ever got married in the first place. 'I hope he didn't upset anyone.'

Karen shrugged. 'Your girl handled him like a pro. She weren't taking any of his crap, tell you that. You did something right with her. Wish you could have a go at my Rory – he's a bit of a pushover for a sob story, that one.' She gazed over at her son, who was listening to Gabriel explaining something with the aid of a diagram drawn on the wet counter in coffee foam. 'Gets him some good tips, mind. He *listens* to people. Still, if he's going to work in sound, I suppose it goes with the territory. Not much good not liking listening to people if it's your job.'

I drained my mug. 'Well, I suppose I ought to get back. I emailed the supply agency this morning and I should check to see whether they've got back to me about going onto their register.'

Karen sniffed. 'You needn't sound so keen,' she said, her tone heavy with irony. 'Did you not always want to be a teacher? Poppy said it's what you've done since she was born, practically. Must be a vocation, cos buggered if I know why anyone would do it otherwise. *One* teenager is more than I can cope with, never mind thirty of them.'

I thought of my classes. Not thirty, far smaller in the exclusive school I taught at, but air hot with rising hormones and clouds of Arpège perfume inherited from 'Mummy'. No deliberate misbehaviour but an attitude of careless privilege, as though the French language could be inherited along with acres of Yorkshire and a flat in Knightsbridge and didn't need to be learned.

'No, no vocation,' I said. 'It was pretty much the only thing I could do with a degree in French literature and a small child. So I took my teaching qualification and at least it meant

I was always there for Poppy in the school holidays.' The words 'because her father certainly wasn't' didn't, I felt, need to be said. Karen had been a single mother all Rory's life; she knew how it was.

Outside a particularly savage thrust of wind rattled the doors and windows and cast sea spray up the planking. Karen made a face. 'We'd better all get out of here before high tide,' she said. 'Cos the car park isn't going to be much fun if this carries on.' And then she looked at me with her head on one side. 'Still can't see you as a teacher. What did you want to be when you grew up?'

The question took me aback. What had I wanted to be? My mother's desire for me to be a competition rider had swept any childish career dreams off the face of the map. It was just so implicitly understood that I'd take over my father's rides as he got older; he'd take up training and teaching pupils and I'd compete the horses for him. Me doing anything else had been unthinkable. Even, it seemed, by me.

'When you was little,' Karen went on, 'what did you think you'd end up doing? Me, now, I was going to marry Jamie Theakston and be a model whilst designing my own make-up range.' She looked around the café. The other visitors were packing up their things and leaving, Summer trailing around behind them in the presumed hope that they were about to drop laden plates on the floor in front of him. 'Think I had a lucky escape all round.'

A small memory, just the faintest tweak. Me sitting in bed, reading set after set of pony books. Old, modern, I'd just gobbled them up, got annoyed with the inaccuracies and some of the endings. Wished I could have lived the lives of some of the heroines, even those who desperately wanted ponies and couldn't have them. I'd have traded my Pony Club

membership and three We
and friendship groups. 'I wa
said, each word individually g
books for people like me.'

'You'll have to have a go, then.'
clearing the table. 'And you'll have
now and then. Bunch of us girls from
Steepleton, we gets together every now
pub on the Bridport road for a few gins a   You'd
have a great time. And you can tell us all abo   ir books.'

'Writing books for children won't earn me enough to keep
the cottage ticking over though.' I stood up too. 'I have to go
back to teaching to keep the bills paid.' I didn't mention going
out to the pub. It was the first time anyone had offered me
friendship that wasn't contingent on having a daughter the
same age, or working at the same place, or because I had a
rich exotic husband, and I needed to think about it. Maybe
savour it a little. Karen wanted to be friends with *me*. It was a
new concept.

Karen sighed. 'Yeah. But it's nice to have dreams, isn't it?
You won't be a mum all your life, after all.'

* * *

I thought about that on the drive home, through the wild
night. After I'd dropped Gabriel at Thea's flat in Steepleton,
where the wind was swiping the tops off the waves and
sending foam the height of the houses on the seafront, I drove
slowly up over the steep clifftop road, mulling over Karen's
words.

She was right. I wouldn't always be a mum, and the end of
that particular section of my life was coming into view

dly. Poppy's first ten years had seemed to last
y; I remembered fretting about the loss of freedom,
nability to put her down and go on with life as it had
been before. But I'd been so young... *so young.* Little more
than a teenager myself when she was born, I'd not really got a
handle on all that life had to offer. I'd spent so much of it
either trying to please my mother or trying to appease her
that I hadn't really had chance for a good look round at all the
potential.

And now that chance was beginning to glimmer over the
horizon. Karen had been right about other things too. I wasn't
really a committed teacher. I hated the paperwork, the hours
of marking and report writing, and, whilst I enjoyed the
actual standing-in-front-of-a-class part, I didn't flatter myself
that I had any particular flair for it. Teaching in a private girls'
school wasn't really a preparation for huge inner-city compre-
hensives, so I lacked that edge of flexibility.

I turned the car down the little lane towards the cottage
and the wind died to a thrashing and roaring in the treetops
as we reached the protection of the curved shoulder of the
hill. Some of the trees were still hanging grimly on to foliage,
as though in denial of the coming winter, and leafy branches
whipped to and fro in a parody of life over my head. Detritus
littered the lane, some quite large lumps of tree dotted the
road surface and I had to steer carefully around them, the
tyres crunching over acorns and chestnuts as I went.

The cottage was invisible in its absolute darkness, but a
glimmer of light spilled out from between the curtains of the
caravan. It illuminated the outline of Patrick, who had tucked
himself against the hedge, head down, seeking whatever
shelter was afforded by the tightly packed hawthorn near the
gate.

I hated to admit it, but it was quite nice to know that someone was out there. That, should Mr Coombes' ghost be dragging itself forlornly around the hallway of Harvest Cottage, at least there was someone to hear me scream. I parked the car in the pull-in space, climbed over the gate and went in through the back door to the relative warmth of the kitchen. The front door seemed too far away from the light, the hedges just a little too overgrown, and, even though I was *absolutely positive* there were no such things as ghosts – well. The back door was nearer.

I didn't turn on the light. The switch was at the far side of the room, convenient for coming in through the main house, but not much use if you came in the back way, so I took my coat off in the dark. I was in the process of hanging it on the hook behind the door, appreciating the still air and the smell of recent baking, when I heard the noise. A deep thump, from the door to the house beyond. Slow, scraping footsteps along the bare sanded boards. And through the half-open doorway, the image of a dark, hunched shape, pulling itself along the hallway wall, groping towards the unlit kitchen.

I was torn between screaming and arming myself. In the end I managed a little whimper and to close my fist around the only thing to hand, one of the scented candles that I'd bought in Bridport that were decorating the work surface. I'd raised it above my head – although what good it would do against a walking spectre I wasn't sure; maybe I could patchouli oil and lily them back into the next world – when the groping figure slid into the room.

It stopped, flat against the wall, making flailing movements. I wasn't sure whether I was supposed to hit it, exorcise it or just lose control of all my bodily functions and run, and was contemplating doing all three simultaneously, when the dark figure spoke.

'Where the hell is the light switch in this godforsaken place?'

It was Luc.

* * *

Embarrassment at my relief had forced me to make tea, and Luc and I sat at the table, on opposite sides, me with hands cupped gratefully around the warmth of my thick mug, whilst Luc stared into the rising steam from his Earl Grey, no milk and, to his evident dissatisfaction, no slice of lemon either. I'd rather facetiously offered him a piece of chocolate orange as the nearest equivalent, but he hadn't even smiled.

'So why were you sitting in my house in the dark?' I finally asked him, when I'd had enough of admiring his fashionable new jacket and noticing the fact that his hair was definitely thinning on top.

'You don't lock the doors.'

'That's not really a reason, though, is it?'

'And I could not find the light switch.'

I put my mug down rather harder than I'd intended. 'Luc, this is *my house*. You don't have the right to just come in whenever you feel like it, just because it's not locked. Otherwise I'd have half the neighbourhood in here every day.' I had a brief image of coming home to find Granny Mary happily installed in front of the log-burner and wondered if I shouldn't start locking the doors more often.

He sighed a deep Gallic sigh. 'Poppy, she is being a *waitress*!'

I waited, but I was obviously meant to know what he was

getting at. 'Yes, she is,' I said carefully. Luc had always had a habit of having only half a conversation, convinced that I was filling my half with corroborating evidence and agreement, and he seemed to regard any kind of attempt at contradicting him to be beneath his notice.

'Pah!' His cup went down too now. 'She cannot be a waitress! She will have a trust fund from Maman when she is twenty-five; she will not be waiting on tables! She ought to be finding herself a career, something that will use her talents, not serving cakes and tea to fat old women and their spaniels!'

I breathed carefully. 'Two things, Luc. Firstly, she's fourteen. Earning money as a waitress is practically a rite of passage; what she's doing at fourteen is no indication of what she's going to be doing for the rest of her life. And secondly, *it's nothing to do with us*. She will do what she wants to do, and us trying to make her... oh, I don't know, be an accountant or something, is not going to work.'

'But if she thinks she will be a waitress she will not work hard at school!' He practically wailed the words. 'She will throw away her education for an apron and a way with muffins!'

His chair squealed on the tiled floor as he inched it closer to the table, elbows digging into the scrubbed pine with the intensity of his desire not to have his daughter fall into a life of menial tasks. It had been fine for his *wife* to perform them, of course.

'Don't you ever tell her she's got a trust fund coming to her – that would be the death of any kind of ambition.' I thought of my previous students and their airy hand-waves as to the necessity to earn a living. 'Honestly, nothing kills ambition like knowing you're going to be rich anyway. It forces you into a life of interior design and wedding planning. And anyway, it's entirely up to Poppy what she does with her life. The harder we try to persuade her not to be a waitress, the more she will dig her heels in and sign up at catering college.'

'She is very much like you in that respect,' Luc observed, but he'd picked up his cup again.

I restrained myself from my urge to throw my mug at him. 'She's got years to decide. But it's up to her.' The words echoed round the kitchen and I wondered if anyone had ever said them about me. Whether my mother and father had ever had this discussion regarding my career. Probably not. My mother had been very forceful in her belief that I could be a successful three-day-event rider, and my father had rarely argued with her. He'd preferred the horses to people anyway; we'd hardly ever had a conversation that hadn't had the words 'martingale' or 'overreach boots' in it. He'd loved me, but I had an insufficient number of legs for him to be able to relate to me and he had deferred, as he had with most things, to my mother in the matter of my upbringing. 'It is up to her,' I said again and more definitely.

'I am not happy.' Luc stood up now, straightening his, I now noticed, significantly bulkier than they used to be shoulders. Middle-aged spread was not purely the province of the British, I realised, and smiled secretly. 'Poppy knows I think she should be studying. She will never meet a suitable man by waiting on tables.'

'Yes, Karen said you'd been to the café,' I said neutrally.

He stared at me, clearly trying to work out whether I was being sarcastic or not. 'I was telling Poppy that she must work harder at school. Get a good degree, business management, perhaps. Maybe she can come and help me to manage the vineyard, for some experience. There are many in my circle that would be a good husband for her, and she would be useful to them. Although, of course, she will not be able to work when her children are born.'

My mother had been the opposite. Trying to discourage me from spending hours on my homework or meeting 'suitable boys' when I could be out in the manège, with her shouting, 'His hocks are trailing! Use your *legs*, darling!' and flicking at me with the lunge whip. In some ways the opposite of Luc, and yet, in other ways, exactly the same. I wondered now, for the first time, if she'd always intended me to marry Luc, and that was why she'd sent me out to France, and been so happy for us to get together. Maybe she'd planned it all along? It was a disconcerting thought that I'd been coupled up in as premeditated a way as she would have sent a good mare to a prize-winning stallion.

'I want Poppy to find out for herself what she wants to do,' I said, quietly but firmly. 'If that turns out to be a lifetime of serving teas, then so be it.' I took his cup and pointedly put it in the sink. 'Now, I think you should go before the weather gets any worse.'

Luc switched topics with the practised ease of a man who could never be in the wrong for long. 'Ah, Katie, you should not have bought this place. What you need is somewhere close to town, where there are shops and galleries. What is there out here in the wilds of Dorset, huh? Nothing but mud and a bad phone signal!'

'No, that's what *you* need. Not me. We're fine here, Luc.' *And it's a far less dangerous place for a fourteen-year-old girl*, I wanted to add, but didn't. He'd grown up with all the self-confidence and self-esteem of a monied chateau owner; he didn't understand that danger didn't always come with knives and demand your wallet.

Luc waved an insouciant hand, indicating, probably mostly by accident, the woodlice currently gossiping along the skirting and the single bulb swinging in the draught that came in under the door. 'I know you will do the right thing, Katie.' And then he was gone, wafting out of the front door, which swung closed behind him with a crash that seemed as though even the house was grateful that he'd gone.

'The phone signal isn't *that* bad,' I muttered, when the echoes of Luc's leaving had died down.

I made myself another cup of tea and congratulated myself on standing up to Luc, even though he hadn't really taken any notice. Time and distance and, yes, the need to defend this damp little corner of the county were doing me good. They reduced his glamour and the feel that I needed to appease him, to keep him on side. I'd always felt that I needed Luc, somehow. Needed him as an ally in bringing up Poppy. But now I was beginning to see that I needed to be *her* ally; we could be a team against her father's determined sexism and over-privilege. If she wanted to be a waitress all her life, then I would make absolutely sure that was what she did. Even though every atom of my being might be screaming at me about lost opportunities and wasted potential, I would be *damned* if a single word would give me away.

I knew what it was like to be on the other side. Poppy would never find out.

My phone buzzed on the table and I picked it up.

It was Gabriel. 'Are you back at the cottage?' His voice was distorted and broken over a line that crackled and I mentally pulled a face at Luc.

'Yes. It's blowing a real gale tonight, isn't it?' Crackle. Silence. I looked down at the handset; Gabriel was, according to the phone, still on the line. 'Hello?'

'Sorry. I think it's the weather, happens round here some-times. Rain gets in the mast, or something. Sure you're all right down there? Granny Mary still in the orchard? Not...' crackle crackle '... halfway up an oak tree?'

I glanced out through the kitchen window. The little cara-van, tucked snugly into the angle of the hedge, still threw a narrow blade of light across Patrick's withers. He was eating from his hay net, which was swinging wildly from the apple tree, like a piñata for ponies.

'We're fine here.'

Another silence, but I could hear him breathing. 'Is it – I mean, would it be all right if I came over tomorrow? I'd like to see you. To... talk.'

The thought blossomed in my mind of Gabriel sitting on my couch in the tiny front room, the light of the log-burner flickering over the angles of his cheekbones and reflecting from his eyes. 'Oh, yes,' I said, a little too quickly and breath-lessly, and then, catching at myself, 'that would be nice. Would you like a lift?'

He laughed. 'It's going to be worse tomorrow. You stay put. I'll walk down over the cliffs.'

'Be careful.' I'd said it before I thought.

'It's okay, Katie,' he said gently. 'I'm hardly going to be standing on the cliff edge leaning into the wind and going "wheeeee", am I? I've known this place all my life. I know how to stay safe.'

The image of him, all dark and firelit, faded before the image of Poppy and Rory standing on the top of the cliff that led down to Warram Bay, leaning into the wind and going 'wheeee'. I shook my head hard. 'It will be lovely to see you,' I said, quietly. I remembered that kiss in the café car park, that had promised... something. The touch of his fingers on my skin, the lines of his long body in that black coat. 'Really lovely.'

'Great! I'll bring...' But the line died into a crackling and then silence. I tidied the kitchen, wondering what he was bringing. It could be anything, from another bottle of WKD to his sister, which made me worry about whether I should tidy the whole cottage or just change the sheets on my bed. He wouldn't bring Thea, would he? I mean, that kiss – there had been the weight of a whole life in that kiss. And also just the tiniest tickle of anticipation of pleasure in the press of his lips and the fingertip touch against my face. It had definitely *not* had an aura of 'let me bring my sister' about it.

15

I lay awake listening to the wind snaking through the branches of the trees lining the lane outside and the hiss and rush of the ford at the bottom. Occasional rain battered my window and sneaked in through the gaps in the sash that were letting enough of the gale through to wobble my curtains. Odd crashes, sounding like dinosaurs reanimated for the night, were more likely to be branches falling than stegosaurs roaming the woods, but my imagination was on overdrive here in the gusty dark.

The cottage was noisy enough to be another person. It seemed to breathe, an inhale as the first rush of wind hit the walls followed by a noisy exhale up the chimneys and through the gaps in the doors, then the rattling cough of twigs, acorns and conkers clattering onto every hard surface. There was a curious comfort in the anthropomorphisation of the place, I thought, snuggling deeper under my covers and listening to yet another cloud burst overhead sending pebbles of rain bouncing off the windows. As though the cottage wouldn't let anything more than the insidious draught get to me through its thick walls and inadequate glazing.

I fell asleep briefly, cocooned snugly under my two duvets, and dreamed storm-tossed dreams about being at sea and huge waves threatening to topple my boat. When I woke suddenly with a jerk that pulled the bottom duvet up over my head, it was to moonlight wriggling its way through a gap in the clouds and illuminating the night like an eldritch lantern.

Sleep had become an impossibility. My brain was in a weird state of double alert, half on edge because of the booming storm and half in a state of nervous excitement. That kiss in the car – Gabriel saying that he was besotted with me... It was all just... And the windows were dancing in their frames with the force of the wind that also howled down the chimney and was cut to noisy shreds by the tattered branches of the trees outside my window. Too much for sleep. Well, if Gabriel remarked on the dark circles under my eyes he was not the man I thought he was. I got up and stalked through the house, much as the putative ghost of Mr Coombes would have done, had it been both a vengeful and nocturnal shade and real. The draught accompanied me at my ankles, like a chilly cat, pushing its way against my bare skin and making me wish I'd put on a pair of socks.

The kitchen was warmer than upstairs and a little shred of light was still coming from the caravan, highlighting Patrick, now grazing on the upwards slope, and the fact that a pool of water had collected halfway up the wheel hubs. I half considered going out and talking to Granny Mary, but then reconsidered. She might well be asleep and have just left the light burning and me appearing in her doorway, unslept and to the accompaniment of a backing gale, might not be the best awakening for an elderly lady.

I made tea and took it into the living room, where the log-burner still held a faint glow under the pile of ash and gave off a little bit of heat. Downstairs the storm felt as though it was a little further away; the windows were protected by the growth of hedge and, although this meant that stems tracked and flailed across the glass, at least I couldn't hear the worst of it in the height of the trees. Moonlight came and went like an undecided spouse, riding the gale on interestingly shaped clouds, and I wished I'd given in to Poppy's request for a dog. Or that we had got a kitten or two. Even a hamster would have been company in this long, loud night.

I wasn't frightened, not exactly, although Luc's unexpected arrival earlier had set me a little on edge and the storm was making me jump every now and again. I felt, I thought, tucking my feet up on the sofa and pulling the throw over me against the chill, *safe*. Safely settled within these old walls. It struck me again, as I sipped at my rapidly chilling tea, that I'd never really had that safe feeling before. Oh, maybe years ago, when Dad had been alive, in the big farmhouse with the spaniels sleeping on my bed and the horses calling to one another from paddocks and loose boxes. Maybe I'd felt safe as a child, but only as a very young one. As soon as I'd been able to ride independently my mother had had me up on beasts that had always felt just a little bit scary. Not for me the placid old schoolmaster ponies. Once I'd grown out of my Pony Club Welsh cobs – and they hadn't exactly been the steadiest of beasts – I'd been moved on to the horses that my dad had been sent to school. Half a tonne of nervous tension with the speed and ability to cart me off for miles over hedges if someone rustled a plastic bag in the same postcode. I'd ridden them, of course, come to understand their twisty imaginations and tendencies to run first and think later, and I'd had the ability to sit out their panics and alarums. But it hadn't been what you might call restful.

Then it had been the precarious existence of living with my hair-trigger mother, and then the peripatetic Luc. Trying not to say the wrong thing that might set off an argument or, in my mother's case, the dismissive hand-wave. Always just a little bit primed, always just a little bit *waiting*. I'd spent my entire life up to now constantly on the edge of a precipice. Now, here, was the first time I felt as though I'd moved away from the drop.

So, feeling reassured and remarkably cosy considering there was undergrowth trying to get into the house, I fell asleep on the sofa.

* * *

I gradually woke up, aware that branches were still tapping on the window. When I turned over on the sofa, sleep-dribble sticking the throw to my cheek and my hair scrobbled about with the friction of the velvet cushions, it was to see Gabriel knocking gently on the glass and smiling in at me. When he saw that I'd noticed him, he held up a bottle and a bag and mouthed 'breakfast' at me, but I was too busy being horribly embarrassed to really take much note of his forethought. I did consider pulling the blanket over my head and pretending to be ill, and making a large laminated sign to stick on the wall to remind myself to draw the curtains in future when I slept on the couch, but neither of these things would be much use now he'd seen me, so I stumbled my way to the front door and opened it.

'The door's not locked. You could just walk in,' I said,

rather grumpily, into the wind that was projecting small brown birds into the air over the hedge behind him.

'That would be rude,' he replied. 'And scary. Now, I've bought croissants and some nice wine. Shall we pretend to be French and have both now, or just have breakfast and save the wine for... later?'

I didn't miss that little pause. Just as I didn't miss the look he gave me, half shy and half laughing, with his wonderful brown eyes crinkling up under the big glasses and the wind tangling his hair so that he looked all wild and romantic and a little bit sexy. A bit Aidan Turnerish, if Aidan Turner had to wear really thick glasses and looked as though he needed to see daylight a bit more.

'Let's start with croissants, shall we? I'll put the kettle on if you light the log-burner.' I wrapped the throw around me to cover the fact that I was wearing fluffy pyjamas, although there was really not much sartorial improvement in wearing a fluffy blanket, and shuffled my way through to the kitchen. Patrick was peering in through the window, although I could see that Mary had filled up his hay net and done his water, so I wasn't sure why. Maybe he thought he was some kind of equine chaperone, who had to keep an eye on me to make sure I wasn't being unfaithful to him with a Shetland in here or something.

I made tea and wandered back to find Gabriel trying to arrange himself on the sofa. 'Sorry. I was trying to find the most macho way to sit,' he said, standing up again to drape his big black coat over the sofa arm, where it hung like a wilted vampire. 'Something about this sofa makes me sit like I'm about to ride side-saddle.' He sat again, this time leaning forward with his elbows on his thighs. 'And since I'm already only a frock away from actually being a woman...'

'Don't,' I said, putting the tea down.

'Don't?'

'Don't do yourself down. Don't feel that you have to be more manly than Bruce Willis. There is nothing wrong with the way you are, Gabriel. Not all women want a man who can throw them over their shoulder and run four miles whilst building a shed with the other hand.'

He stared at me. 'That was a horrible sentence, Katie.'

'I know what I mean. And I think you do too.' I sat next to him and took the proffered croissant. 'I've done my time. Luc is French, which gives him an excuse, but, my God, I'll take a man who brings me breakfast over a man who looks good in a ripped vest and knows his way around an AK-47 any day.'

'But I crochet and quilt for a living!' He took the tea.

'That doesn't matter. Someone has to, why not you? And from the things I've seen that you make, you are bloody good at it too. So why *wouldn't* you do something that you are good at, just because it's not seen as something men usually do? Nobody really turns a hair at a woman doing anything these days – that's equality. Well, why shouldn't it work the other way too?'

He sighed. 'Yes. I've been caught in the double-standards trap, haven't I?' He put the tea down and turned on the sofa to face me. 'I've been caught in a lot of things. But I really, really like you, Katie.'

My heart started to drum. 'But you know about me. Me killing my dad.'

'You know that was an accident. You're using it as something to hide behind, like you use Poppy,' he said, very matter-of-factly, whilst shifting around on the snaggy velvet as though his trousers were Velcro. 'You've had a complicated life, Katie, but, and I can't stress this too much, mostly because I've got half a croissant lodged in my molars, *it wasn't your fault.*'

'I think we should get a dog,' I said. Changing the subject was all I could think of to do. 'Poppy really wants one and after last night – well, I think something else alive in the house would be a good thing. But I'm out so much, and if I have to travel for work...'

'There are dog walkers, even out here.' He followed my switch of topic easily, and I fell just a little bit in love with him then. The tea in my hand began to slop over the rim of my mug. 'And dogs are good company. Just, you know, don't go for something like Tansy and Davin's Brian – he's not really a dog, he's Victor Meldrew in a furry suit.'

'Gabriel...' I wasn't sure what I had been going to follow this up with. I was just standing there in front of him, watching him wriggle around against the pull of the velvet, looking all dark and approachable and leggy in his black jeans and sweater, like a windswept Goth. He stood up.

'I know,' he said, and his voice was very quiet, almost inaudible over the sound of the wind trying to break in. 'I know.'

And he reached out and pulled me against him; his mouth was warm and his breath tasted of croissant and his hands were so gentle against my skin. He held my face, cupping it in his long fingers, and I could feel his heart sledge-hammering his ribs, even over the feel of mine doing the same.

We stood like this for, what? Minutes? Hours? Breathing one another in. Handing one another all our insecurities silently, accepting them and taking comfort. We only broke apart when a log thumped and fell in the burner behind me and I realised that something else needed to happen.

I didn't need to speak. Just looped my fingers around his wrist and began to walk and he followed, not pulled along, just... walking. Complicit. I didn't stop until we reached my bedroom.

'I think...' I said, and tailed off. The bed looked crumpled. Inviting.

He looked at it too. 'I think so too,' he said, and suddenly we were kissing again, not the decorous, reassuring kisses of downstairs, but kisses that were heavy with desire. Kisses that didn't confine themselves to mouths but began to wander, and soon clothes were extraneous and then not there, and we were tumbling into one another, falling into the – thankfully clean – tangled sheets as though someone had released some kind of aphrodisiac gas into the room that we were powerless to resist.

I don't know why I'd expected a man who looked as he did to be inexperienced. His general diffidence, I suppose – his certainty that women wouldn't want a man who could colour-match fabric and crochet a throw had given me to think that he might have been limited in his dating pool. He might have been, of course, but whoever he *had* dated had been pretty knowledgeable. And a good teacher. I tried to keep images of Karen out of my head, and after a while it was easy to keep *everything* out of my head except this gorgeous man and the things he could do to the female body. I said, 'Oh, God,' and 'Gabriel!' so many times and with such fervour that anyone listening would have thought I was having a particularly intense religious experience, which was pretty close to what was happening.

He, in his turn, seemed to enjoy himself too. At the risk of being indiscreet, I'd have to say that, in bed, there was *nothing* soft about Gabriel Hunter.

And afterwards... ah, afterwards. That was almost the best bit, for a given definition of 'best bit' because the foregoing bits had been pretty damn spectacular. Afterwards, he swaddled me in the duvet and padded downstairs wearing my dressing gown, slim wrists and hairy legs protruding, and returned with the bottle of wine, which turned out to be quite posh champagne, and we lay together in a casual acceptance of limbs, taking it in turns to drink out of the bottle.

'This is really good,' I said, swigging in a very unladylike way that my mother would definitely not have approved of. Although I thought I'd rather shot my bolt today in 'things my mother would approve of'.

'Well, you were married to a guy who owned vineyards. I was hardly going to bring a bottle of Lambrini, was I?' He raised his eyebrows at me. With his glasses off his eyes were huge. So dark they were practically mirrors, and prolifically lashed in a way that Poppy spent hours with expensive mascara trying to create.

'It wouldn't have mattered,' I said quietly. 'And I didn't just mean the alcohol.'

'No.' His voice was equally quiet. 'I know you didn't.' And the neck of the bottle was replaced by his mouth as he kissed me again. 'I wanted you to have a bit of romance. I wanted it to be special.'

'I'm glad I bothered to change the sheets, then,' I said. 'Although I rather think I may have to change them again now.'

A stronger-than-usual gust of wind hit the side of the house, caught in the guttering, which flapped, and sent all the windows into a spasm. There was a huge crash from somewhere outside and Gabriel climbed out of bed to peer through the rattling pane.

'Massive branch down across the lane,' he said. 'That old oak about fifty metres up towards the main road. And all the road people are busy trying to clear the Bridport and Dorchester roads, so we'll have to wait for a passing farmer with a tractor to drag it away. And what with the ford being flooded, looks like we're trapped here. Oh dear, whatever shall we do?'

'I can think of one or two things,' I said and raised the bottle to him. The champagne was going to my head rather. I let it.

A while later we surfaced again. 'I'm starving,' I said. 'Shall I cook us something?'

'Mmm.' He stretched his long body. I was amazed at how well he fitted in here, as though I'd chosen something in the homeware department of an exclusive shop and couldn't stop looking at it in my actual house. 'Also, I think we ought to tell Granny Mary.'

I stopped, halfway into a fleecy top. 'About...?' I indicated his nakedness and mimed a sort of bouncy-bouncy action. '*Really?*'

Gabriel lounged into an upright position. 'About us, being together. I think she'll approve, you know.'

'How will we be able to tell?'

'She'll be mildly less acerbic. Come on, we can pop over to the caravan and then I'll give you a hand in the kitchen.' Then, reacting to my raised eyebrows, 'What? I told you, I'm great at all indoor activities.'

'Oh, aren't you just?' I said, with feeling.

'Oh, hush, you'll embarrass me. And, given what we've just been doing, that's going to take some doing.'

We laughed at one another all the way down the stairs. There was something looser about him now; he looked less locked into his worry. Maybe now that I'd graphically proved to him that I didn't find him unattractive or less than a man he found it easier to relax. Had he not truly believed me up until now? I didn't know, but made a mental note to ask him. Later.

We splashed out across the orchard. Patrick wandered over to nuzzle our pockets, his hooves making a sink-plunger noise in the wet mud and the rain dripping off points in his mane and forelock. His coat lay in wet dreadlocks across his back and his feathers had formed strings down his legs. I patted him and then wiped my hand down my hastily donned jacket; he'd been rubbing against the trees and his neck was green with moss and lichen in the half-light. It was getting rapidly dark now. We'd been in bed for longer than I'd thought and no wonder we were hungry.

'Mary?' Gabriel knocked on the van door.

'What are you doing outside on a day like this?' The grumble approached and the door opened. 'You'll dissolve, the pair of you. Well, come in, don't stand there letting the rain get ahead of you.'

Her gaze flickered off Gabriel and on to me. She didn't say anything, and her eyes barely waited, but I saw her give a half nod and a tiny self-satisfied smile. 'We just thought we'd pop over and, er...' He tailed off.

'Offer to make you a cup of tea,' I finished. She'd clearly already got the picture, and I wasn't sure I wanted to put it into words yet. Gabriel and I, as a couple. How the hell were we going to make this work, when he couldn't drive and lived twenty miles away, and I had a teenage daughter who was *not* going to thank me for proving that I had any kind of life left in me, let alone of the sex variety.

Doubt started to creep over me.

'Don't be bloody daft, I've got a kettle.' Mary began bustling around the stove.

'We've not seen you out and about much. Are you all right?' I asked. There was something somehow slower about Granny Mary today, almost as though movement hurt. Today's band T-shirt, a rather terrifying Megadeth one of skull and crossbones, looked crumpled and her hair hadn't been brushed.

'Of course, you haven't,' she snapped, putting the kettle on the burner. 'Have you seen the weather out there? I've only been going out to check on Patrick. I have no desire to be blown away or soaked to the skin, thank you very much. An acorn between the eyes often offends.'

'Ah. Right.' I sat down on the bench, then held on to the table as the whole caravan swayed in the wind.

'And how are you, young Gabriel?' Mary's voice softened. 'That daft sister of yours improving at all? Or is she still trying to sell knitwear's answer to *The Call of Cthulhu* down in the village?'

'Oh, you know Thea,' he answered comfortably. 'She thinks there's nothing that can't be summoned with a blood sacrifice and a number three hook.'

'Radio says there's trees and branches all over the roads too,' Mary continued, as the kettle began a rather squeaky boil and she fiddled with the mugs. 'It's been a wild one this year. Very atmospheric for the Halloween do down at Steepleton. There'll not be a candle that stays alight down there tonight.'

All three of us looked up at the dark square of window. While I hadn't *forgotten* forgotten that today was Halloween with all that entailed down in the village, I'd managed to keep the actual details from my mind. Admittedly, I'd used energetic sex to distract me, but even so... 'I hope Poppy is all right,' I said, almost as a reflex.

Granny Mary 'tch'd'. 'She'll be having the time of her life.' She put a mug of steaming tea down in front of me.

'That's what I'm afraid of,' I said darkly.

'Ah now, it takes less to have a good time at her age. A cheeky sip of alcohol, bit of a dance and a kiss from someone nice – that's living it up at fourteen, isn't it?' She frowned, bringing another two mugs to the table. 'I'm a bit out of touch, mind.'

Gabriel met my eye. 'Sounds good to me,' he said. 'And the Halloween fair is well supervised – there's loads of people around and most of them are local. It's Halloween in Steepleton, not Carnival in Rio.'

Mary sat down heavily next to me. 'Just because you made daft mistakes when you were young doesn't mean she will,' she said, bending her fingers around her mug of tea. 'She's got her head screwed on right, your daughter. You did a good job with her.'

From Mary this was practically praising me to the skies. I felt a warmth rise up through me. 'Thank you.' I sipped my tea.

'So, you two going to get married, then?' Mary went on, seemingly with no embarrassment. 'Or just go at it like rabbits whenever Poppy's out of the house?'

The warmth got to my cheeks and I felt their heat even through the tea steam. Gabriel made an odd choking noise. 'It's hard,' he said, when tea stopped spraying.

'Yes, I gathered it was.' Mary's tone gave no hint as to whether the double entendre was deliberate or not. 'You not wanting to move him in and all. Sensible though. Your girl's been through enough with moving here. And her pillock of a dad.' She 'tch'd' again. 'Him dressing up and talking like a twenty-year-old when he's not going to see twenty again with a bloody big telescope.'

'He's not all bad,' I said mildly.

'He'll have a ponytail next,' Mary said.

Gabriel and I tried very hard not to look at one another and we sat and drank our tea in the woodsmoke-smelling interior of the van as it rocked with each new gust of wind. There was the occasional thump as lone and particularly adhesive apples finally detached onto the roof and the spider-fingers noise of the hedge trailing on the paintwork. I still felt the tiny glow of pride inside that Mary thought I'd done a good job with Poppy. Karen thought so too, so maybe I had. Maybe I'd finally got something right. Been good enough at something.

Beside me I became aware of Mary slumping onto the bench seat and I wondered if she'd fallen asleep. I had to admit it was slightly soporific, the dim light from the lantern on the table, the gentle rock and roll of the van against the wind and the warmth from the stove, but when I turned to check whether she was actually asleep or just relaxed and dozing, what I saw made me shout and jump up.

'Gabriel! Something's wrong!' Mary was awake, but staring rigidly ahead. One side of her face seemed to have melted down like candle wax, her mouth pulled towards her shoulder. 'Mary?'

Gabriel was on his feet now too. 'Mary?' He spoke more gently than I had. Mary's eyes moved and she made a 'gggggg' sound, but that was all. 'Let's lay you down,' he said. With seemingly little effort, he picked Granny Mary up and carried her to the back of the caravan, where he laid her down on her little box bed. Her mouth seemed to be straining as if she was trying to speak, her right arm was clenched tight against her body but her left was flailing about, trying to indicate something.

'Another stroke?' I asked, half under my breath. I didn't know why I was whispering; there were only three of us in here and one of us clearly already knew what was happening.

'We need an ambulance.' Gabriel was groping in his pockets. 'My phone's out of charge.'

I remembered all the first-aid training that I'd been forced to undergo as a teacher. Speed was of the essence in cases of stroke, I remembered that much. 'Mine is in the kitchen.' I ran, down the slippery steps, through the mud, and grabbed my phone from the kitchen worktop, where it lay inert. Dialled 999 as I ran back through the orchard.

The line crackled into life and I blurted our emergency as I dashed back into the van, where Gabriel was crouched next to Mary, holding her left hand.

The operator crackled. Took the call but her responses were so broken that I couldn't understand her. Gabriel took the phone from me. 'No, not an ambulance,' I heard him say. 'Hello? Can you hear me?'

'Got... details. Ambulance... way... take time... roads difficult.'

'No! We need a helicopter! Our road is blocked!'

Mary made the 'gggggg' noise again and he passed the phone to me. 'Did you get that?' I was shouting, although I didn't know why. 'There's a flood at the bottom of the road and a tree down at the top!'

'Amb...' crackle crackle '... despatch... keep... warm.'

'WE NEED THE HELICOPTER!' I yelled, although volume wasn't the issue. By the time an ambulance got here and they'd negotiated getting a stretcher around the fallen tree, walked down to the house and walked back... well. FAST, that was what they said about strokes, wasn't it?

Now Gabriel had joined in and we were booming, 'WE NEED THE HELICOPTER!' as though the phone didn't exist and we were trying to make the despatch unit hear.

'Ambulance... been... on way.' And the line went dead. Whether we'd been cut off or she'd moved on to another call, I didn't know.

Gabriel and I looked at one another. Between us, Granny Mary flailed a bit more and then lay silent. 'Oh, God,' I said.

'There's no use them sending an ambulance.' Gabriel spoke quickly, breathlessly. 'It'll take too long. We need to call them back on a landline.' He looked at me hopefully.

I shook my head. 'Just mobiles in this house.'

'Where's the nearest farm?'

I jerked my head. 'Over the cliffs that way. But I don't know whether they have a landline either.'

Gabriel was rubbing Mary's hand. He gave her a quick glance. 'Steepleton, then,' he said, with the air of one making a decision. 'I'll run. Over the clifftops. It's only a couple of miles.'

The gale struck the side of the caravan and we swayed again. I looked down at Mary. Her eye was still open, watching us, her face sunken and distorted around it. 'We need to be faster. My car... could I get it around the tree?'

A quick shake of his head. 'Nope. It's gone down in the thick hedging and the field gates are locked. Not even a 4 x 4 would do it. You need some kind of ATV.'

Outside the van, Patrick blew down his nose, a snort that rattled the air.

'Could I get the car through the ford? Go round that way?'

He shook his head again and stood up. 'I'll run,' he said. 'It's better than doing nothing.'

'We've got an ATV,' I said and my voice shook. 'There's Patrick.'

Gabriel was doing up his jacket. 'I can't ride,' he said.

'No, but I can. If we gallop over the cliff, we can get there faster than you running. And Patrick will be less likely to get swept over the cliffs in the wind.' I was half out of the van already.

'But you...'

'Yes, I know.' The sick horror was staying nicely down around my stomach. *The last time I sat on a horse... the last time I rode... I wasn't good enough.* Over the shriek of the wind I could still hear that horse scream. That dull thump. 'But I can't see another way. Running will take too long. He can gallop faster than you can run.' I'd got to the kitchen now. Pulled my coat down off the hook and scraped myself into it.

'But there's no saddle.'

It was as though practicality cut in and shoved everything else out of the way. With my coat firmly zipped I went back to the van, to the little box on the outside where the driving harness was kept. My hands were steady as I pulled the driving bridle, with its intricate bit and the blinkers, out of the box and smelled that smell of wet leather and saddle soap that had been the perfume of my childhood. 'Stay with Mary.'

As though there had never been any break in my experience, I caught hold of Patrick's mane, slid the headpiece behind his ears and the bit into his unresisting mouth. Gathered up the long, long driving reins and vaulted onto the broad back, to both Patrick and Gabriel's evident surprise.

And I remembered. As soon as the cold wet under my legs turned to the warmth of a living body, second nature swept in.

I balanced myself, adjusted my seat and shouted, 'Open the gate!' to Gabriel, who ran to swing the big gate that led onto the lane, and we were off. Patrick felt reluctant, stiff and much broader across the back than the horses I'd grown up with, his thick winter coat spongey under my backside and no notable muscle moving beneath me. But when I whispered, 'Sorry,' to him and kicked him on, he sprang out into a trot that was practically jaunty, and then we were out onto the lane, Gabriel looking up at me as I passed him.

'Just before where the tree's down you go right, there's the footpath that takes you onto the clifftop,' he shouted over the wind. 'Just go left when the footpath reaches the cliff. And stay away from the edge!'

I hardly slowed down to listen. In my head the dichotomy raged; something I hadn't done since I was fourteen, swore I'd never do again, the promise I'd kept for twenty years being overcome by the sheer strength of childhood memory. The way Patrick's fore end rose and fell as I kicked him hard into a canter, the feel of his hindquarters pushing us along. The slide and clop of his unshod hooves on the tarmac of the lane, the whippy feel of his mane as it flopped with each stride. I *knew* this. I could *do* this.

He was slow, slower than anything I'd ridden since I was about six. His canter was straight out of a rocking-horse factory, but so easy to sit that I hardly had to think about it and could concentrate on the steering, with the long reins bunched up in each hand. I leaned across the piebald withers, pushing him on with hands and seat as we rode on into the gale, tears stripped from my eyes by the force of the wind.

I slowed as we approached the fallen tree. Patrick blew once, twice, then his head came up and he fell into an easy trot as I steered him right, off the road and down into the narrow footpath that Gabriel had mentioned. Down, splashing through mud, no faster than a trot because I couldn't see underfoot, enjoying the relative shelter, then bursting out onto short cropped grass, turning left, with the sound of the sea booming somewhere underneath us and Patrick was galloping, stretching his chunky body into the wind as I urged him on.

The wind took the breath from my lungs and the water from my eyes; it was coming at us from seemingly every side as we thudded along the bare stretch of grass. Patrick balanced himself like a pro – he even jumped a small log that lay in our path, as though he was enjoying himself. As we breasted a small rise, I saw a lone house, and then, further down the hillside, a beaten track that led down to the flickering lights that bled into the gale and indicated the presence of Christmas Steepleton.

I let Patrick have a breather and walked him along towards the house, then swung down, leaning to open a gate that led onto the track. There was a stile but I wasn't quite sure of Patrick's jumping capability and figured that it was safer to open the gate than to try and clear it. Patrick stood like a rock as I unhooked the gate, and backed up when asked so I could swing it onto its catch. He'd been well schooled at some point, taught to respond to leg aids as well as my hands, and it seemed that all his experience had cut in at the same point mine had.

We careered down the steep hill into the village proper. Patrick was blowing a lot by this point, sweat was foaming along his neck and under my seat, the cold damp replaced by hot, slick wetness, and we cantered down the tarmac. I *knew* I shouldn't be cantering downhill on an unfit pony, but the image of Mary lying there in the van, face pulled to one side, was uppermost in my mind, and I kicked him on, grateful for the grip of unshod hooves. Metal against this gradient would have seen us slide down into the sea in a shower of sparks.

There were small knots of people walking down the hill. They pressed themselves into the doorways of houses as we passed, flickering lanterns illuminating bits of piebald coat, white sweat, shocked faces. When we got to the turning circle at the bottom of the hill, there was quite a gathering, music playing out through the doors of a building; inside I caught a glimpse of stalls, a snatch of laughter as we fled by, until I pulled Patrick to a puffing, blowing stop outside Thea's shop.

I didn't even pause to tie Patrick up. I just jumped down, my legs achy and jellified, dropped the reins and pounded on the door of the illuminated shop, as spray from the sea swept up over me and the pony. I think I yelled a bit too, until Thea appeared in the window and opened the door, when I gasped, 'Phone. Landline. Now,' and she steered me to an old-fashioned dial telephone behind the till.

The reception was much better on the landline. I managed to give instructions about the helicopter, the fallen tree, the stroke and the despatcher reacted accordingly. When I put the phone down, everything gave up and I sat down hard on the floor of the shop, with Thea standing over me looking puzzled in a multicoloured way, and Patrick backed into the doorway to get away from the waves that were sending spray splashing against the shopfronts.

There was quite a crowd collecting outside now. Despite the furious battering from the spray, several people had gathered around Patrick; from my position on the floor I could see that two of them were Poppy and Rory, and I didn't miss the vital detail that they were hand in hand. I was torn between wanting to fling the door open and demand to know what they thought they were doing, being quietly proud that my daughter had good taste in decent blokes, and wanting to hurl myself flat on the (crocheted, naturally) rug and wail.

Eventually the door tinkled open and Poppy came in. 'Mum? Did you really ride Patrick over here?'

There was a note in her voice that I didn't recognise. 'Yes,' I said, from my position on the surprisingly comfortable floor.

'You... *cow*!' Poppy spun round, a ball of fourteen-year-old fury. 'What, trying to catch me and Rory at something? Well, for your information he's a perfect gentleman, which you wouldn't know anything about because Dad is a dickhead! How could you?' She sounded as though tears were close to breaking through the anger now. 'Oh, God, they are *so* going to take the piss out of me at school! My mum galloped all the way here on that old crock of a horse to try to catch me having it away with *Rory*! I am *dead*!'

I tried to gather my dignity, but couldn't catch hold of enough of it. 'I needed to use the phone. Granny Mary's had another stroke.' I gave myself points for not losing my temper or asking her how she dare call me names. Thea was still standing over me, like a boxing referee wondering if she should count me out, and having someone else there helped me stay in 'responsible mother' persona, although every atom of me wanted to scream back. 'I've left her with Gabriel. You look very nice, by the way.'

She clearly didn't know what to react to first. But she was a teenager, so she went for the compliment. 'Thanks.' She brushed a hand down the velvet sleeve. 'Yeah, loads of people have liked our costumes.' Then she took a deep breath. 'SorryIcalledyoucow,' she muttered.

The crowd outside had collected in the doorway, all trying to stay out of reach of the spray. Waves were hitting the edge of the walkway; the tide must be still coming in. 'I need to get Patrick back,' I said, 'and tell Gabriel what's going on. They're sending a helicopter for Mary.'

Thea looked worried. 'Is she very ill?'

'It's pretty bad, I think.' I flicked a glance at Poppy, hoping Thea would realise that I didn't want to scare my daughter.

'Do you want a drink or something, before you go?' Thea helped me to my feet. 'I've got some herbal tea upstairs.'

'No, thank you. I need to walk back. Patrick gave it all he had to get here. I might have to carry him home, so we need to leave now.' I gave a pathetic little smile.

'We're going back to the party, then.' Poppy headed for the door. 'I mean, if that's okay.'

I looked out, towards the crowd of people carrying lanterns. Now I came to look at them, there were more zombies than you usually see in a seaside town, a fair smattering of sexy witches and some ghosts, one of whom had clearly expected some kind of weather event because he had his wellingtons on under his sheet.

'Yes. You go and enjoy yourself,' I said. Lanterns were being relit, extinguished by the next crashing wave, and relit again. Further down the village I could see a procession lining up, lights on poles and a stilt walker, a couple of fire-eaters flaring off and grinning pumpkin heads everywhere. 'You don't want to miss it. I'll let you know how Granny Mary is later.'

I followed her out of the shop. Patrick clopped sadly and damply up to me, his long reins trailing in the salt water along the seafront. Granny Mary was going to kill me for what would happen to the leather, I thought. Then I remembered. Salt marks on her driving harness was going to be the least of her worries.

I walked Patrick home the way we'd come. Like the last-placed team in a spectacularly badly organised cross-country event we trailed through mud, my feet thoroughly soaked and him sploshing along at my elbow, still stopping to blow and cough heartily every so often. At least the rain had stopped, although the wind was still circling, but I could use Patrick as a windbreak, so it wasn't so bad. I did have to stop and lean on him a few times, but he was also leaning on me; it evened out over the miles. Every so often something – the smell of warm horse, the feel of a nose under my elbow or the way my legs ached – would remind me of the past; years and years of indoctrination were hard to get over. And, apparently, I still knew how to do it. I felt a warm glow of pride, now it was over. *I'd done it.* Bareback too, and I'd not had to do that once my mother was sure that my balance was good; she'd stopped sending me down the jumping lane with no saddle and my arms folded by the time I was ten.

It was a long walk back. But we eventually turned out from the footpath into the lane, where the tree still lay across the road, to see lots of lights, people running about, a huge helicopter in the field beyond the house and Gabriel, standing by the gate with a torch. He jumped as we loomed out of the dark at him.

'Hi! I guess you made it, then.' He waved at the helicopter, where the blades were just beginning to turn, readying for take-off. 'The big whirly bird was a bit of a giveaway.' The torch swung towards my face. 'Are you all right?'

'I need to see to Patrick,' I said, my voice sounding flat under the weight of a new tiredness. 'He needs cooling down properly and then rubbing down. Might need to make him up a mash too.'

'I'd offer to do it for you, but I only recognised three of the words in that sentence.' A hand came out from behind the torch. 'You were incredibly brave.'

My legs were wobbling but the touch of his hand gave me strength to stand. 'No,' I said. 'No. That wasn't brave, Gabriel. Brave is what you do every day. I just rode a horse, something I was born, bred and raised to do. I *don't*, not because I'm scared so much as grateful that I don't have to any more. I'm scared for Poppy after what happened to Dad, but I'm not scared for me, so riding Patrick wasn't brave in the least. *You...*' I sighed, part tiredness, part something else that was almost an exasperation. 'You are facing going blind, you are spending your days making beautiful things even though you think it's going to mean a lifetime of celibacy and you walk around still seeing people who bullied you every day. Now, *that* is brave.'

Then I walked past him, using the bulk of Patrick to shield me from his slightly shocked expression, and began to concentrate on getting the poor horse fit to be put to bed.

16

It was a long, long night. I called up the local news on my laptop, wanting to check that nothing untoward was happening in Steepleton without actually looking as though I was being overprotective, and reports came in every ten minutes or so of trees down on roads, high tides making seafronts impassable, but no mention of trouble at any Halloween celebrations. The fire engines were out from as far afield as Taunton, clearing roads, pumping out flood water, rescuing people trapped or marooned. It seemed we'd been lucky to get the helicopter when we did, as it was now being needed to lift people from crashed cars and flooded seafront properties to hospital.

Gabriel phoned the hospital, but they wouldn't really tell him much. As he wasn't next of kin or even a relative, all we got was, 'The team are doing all they can.' I lit the log-burner and we sat, side by side on the sofa, staring into the flames and occasionally trying to chat, to lighten the atmosphere, but we were both too tightly wrapped in our separate thoughts to lighten things up much.

At last, around the small hours, I suggested we went to bed. Gabriel's head came up. 'I don't know,' he said. 'It doesn't feel... I mean, somehow it feels as though we'd being doing something *wrong*, somehow. Do you understand?'

I did. Almost as though we'd brought Granny Mary's stroke on by making love earlier in the day. 'I'll sleep in Poppy's room. You take my bed,' I said. 'We need to sleep anyway and I'm not sure...' I felt the heat rise up from somewhere in my chest as the memory of the way we'd been last time we'd been in bed together rose up.

Gabriel smiled, a tired, stretched smile. 'Yes. It was fabulous but now is not really the time. And we're both so used to sleeping alone that romantic illusions of us lying all night in one another's arms is probably just a recipe for cramp and a lot of apologising.'

I actually laughed. 'Come on. I need a shower. Is there any more news from the hospital?'

He glanced down at his phone. 'They said they'd ring or text if there was any change. And the signal is still rubbish so I told them text was better. There's nothing here.'

I hoped Granny Mary wasn't lying in a hospital bed feeling deserted. Then the memory of that one open eye, that expression of desperation and hopelessness came back to me. 'I hope she's all right,' I said, with feeling.

'You sound like you've warmed to her a bit.' Gabriel stood up and stretched. 'I told you, she's okay when you get to know her.'

'Do you know...' I was about to ask him if Mary had told him about Rose, about her lost future, but then decided that it was for us to talk about with Mary present, just in case she hadn't told him '... if the roads will be clear by tomorrow?'

'We usually get the main roads cleared quite quickly after

these storms.' If he noticed my verbal stumble, he didn't react. 'Autumn storms and high tides are normal in this part of the world. Not always on quite this scale though.' He waved a hand to indicate the booming windows and the maraca-sound of rain on glass. 'We only get one like this every ten years or so.'

I thought about Poppy and Rory, their fancy costumes, the sight of them hand in hand surrounded by sea spray as they celebrated Halloween. 'In ten years' time I'm going to barricade myself indoors for the duration, then.' Ten years. It was a long time. Anything could happen. Poppy would know about being a trust fund richer – would she stay here in Dorset? Or race back to London? How would her budding romance with Rory turn out? They were so young – but stranger things had happened. My head hurt.

'I need to get clean and go to sleep,' I said.

Gabriel laid a hand on my shoulder, briefly. 'It's been a hell of a day,' he said. 'Things might be very different in the morning.'

* * *

He was partly right. When I woke up, clearly very late as sunlight was streaming in through the window, the storm had vanished as though it had never been. Cold, still light captured untroubled dust motes swirling in the beams; there was a curious silence broken only by the brittle cries of gulls and the nearer and more urgent trill of the blackbird from the hedge. There was also an insistent smell of bacon and toast. With my eyes closed I was almost convinced I was back in the flat in London, with Poppy making herself breakfast and a pile of marking to be done on the table.

The bedroom door swung open. 'I brought food. No news – she's "resting as comfortably as can be expected" apparently. The Bridport road is open, our lane is still blocked, and Karen has said she'll keep Poppy until we can get out and fetch her back.' A tray came into the room with the voice behind it, and a smell of coffee preceding the lot. 'I made food. Sorry, but I was bloody *starving*. I hope I haven't inadvertently cooked a week's worth of dinners for breakfast.'

Gabriel looked amazing, and not just because he was carrying a stack of bacon, some clearly home-made pancake things and a large jug of coffee. He had sleep-rumpled hair and a new growth of stubble, which emphasised his wonderful cheekbones, and a grin that made him look invitingly sexy. Despite all my resolutions, despite everything we'd agreed last night, the smell of the coffee and bacon and frying, I couldn't help myself. I flipped back the corner of the duvet and raised my eyebrows and that was that until the coffee got cold and the bacon was flabby, *and we didn't care*.

The sound of chainsaws woke us. Chainsaws and men calling macho commands to one another to the undertone of a tractor engine rumbling. Gabriel got out of bed and leaned out of the window. 'It's as we feared,' he said gloomily. 'They're taking the fallen log away. I'm afraid we're going to be able to get out.'

The pull of motherhood was happy that I'd be able to fetch Poppy back and have her under my protection again, but the part of me that had revelled in this time with Gabriel crumbled into disappointment. Why couldn't I have both? My daughter wouldn't be at home forever... and maybe that *was* why. While she was here I owed it to her to concentrate on her upbringing – after all, she'd had enough disruption and disorganisation in her life up until now. I'd brought her to Dorset to give her a settled life, one without the threats that the big city constantly held over me. And without, a tiny voice whispered, her father being able to whisk her off to Harrods every weekend or fly her off to the chateau on short notice. Down here, with its marked absence of easy-reach airports, short-notice getaways meant a day on the beach, not a weekend at Longchamp, underage drinking and sophisticated behaviour she wasn't ready for yet.

Gabriel had turned back from the window and was watching me. At least, he didn't have his glasses on but his face was pointing in my direction. I wanted him here. I wanted to have breakfast with him, sit with him, have a *life* with him. How the hell did I tell him that he had to wait another four years before we could do more than snatch moments together?

'How can you see what they're doing down the road when you've not got your glasses on?' I tried to sound jocular rather than accusatory. My inner monologue was my own problem, not his.

He winked. 'Don't have to be able to see to know that it's Andrew Northcote and Bren Gass, also known as "Mr Gassy" to his friends. Was at school with both of them. I predict a later fist fight over who gets to take the wood, and twelve pints up in the pub later to make up. Not much changes round here.' He came over and sat on the edge of the bed. 'Except you coming to Dorset. You've changed everything for me.'

I knew I should reiterate that, at least while Poppy was around, we'd have to keep our distance. Gabriel had already told me he was all right with it; I wanted to wail about how unfair it all was, but was interrupted by my phone pinging a text.

It was Keenan with a rather rambling text, containing a

general indication that the film unit might need to do some more shots to tidy up the storyline, and that he was trying to persuade them that the cottage could be re-dressed and used again for some location work for the next series. I felt a brief loosening of the tight financial screw that lurked somewhere above my stomach and a warm burst of affection towards Keenan. It might not be much, but it would help.

I was just about to tell Gabriel about the text, when the phone buzzed another incoming message. This time it was Karen.

Reckon tree should be cleared soon. Why not meet us up at the pub this evening? Poppy can put in a shift at the café today, she's no trouble. Let me know if there's anything I can do about Granny Mary, if she needs stuff. Hope you and Gabriel are getting on all right trapped up there. 😉

I didn't know whether to be affronted by the winky smiley or not. 'News travels fast,' I said, holding out both messages for him to read.

'Can you make it bigger? Er, the typeface, I mean.' He gave me a slightly shamefaced grin and covered himself with the duvet.

A pause while he read. 'Okay, so be prepared for the entire village to ask intrusive questions and for Poppy to make that lip-wrinkling expression that all teenagers seem to have mastered since I was one. I'm sure we just used to say "gross", but it doesn't seem to be enough nowadays – you've got to do a face to go with it now. There's probably a YouTube tutorial.' He handed me the phone back.

'Gabriel, what are we going to do?'

I couldn't help it. The words burst out of me under the

pressure of being reminded about my daughter's teenagehood and the sheer gorgeousness of this man in my bedroom. Almost as though the two couldn't possibly exist in the same universe.

'Do?' He was rolling up a cold pancake with some bacon.

'About...' I waved a hand. 'Us. This. Poppy.'

He put down the food and knelt beside me. 'Katie, it's okay. I'm not going to want to move in. We've had this discussion. You and Poppy are a unit, I'm just an outlier.'

'But we discussed it all before—' I looked around at the crumpled bed '—before all this happened. Now, I don't know. It's like I've had a taste of what life could be like and can't be.'

Gabriel kissed me very gently. 'Look. It's not ideal. You and Poppy up here in this place that's only a house because calling it a barely weatherproof shack is prejudicial, and me in Bridport with no transport. But we can do it. I can stay at Thea's, come over here and work when Poppy's at school and you can...'

'I haven't even got a *job*!' I wailed. 'I have to have a job to pay the bills! And if you come over when Poppy's at school, that's when I'll be at work!'

Gabriel kissed me again. 'There will be weekends,' he said. 'Poppy will be working in the café, won't she? And holidays?'

'But I don't want her to work there just to keep her out of the way of us... well, doing anything. What if she wants to give up being a waitress?'

Gabriel took a step back. 'Do you want me to say that it's hopeless? That maybe we shouldn't even start something? Because I'm afraid that ship is tooting its way out of harbour, and please don't tell me something horribly clichéd like I shouldn't have feelings for you because of the situation, because that ship, likewise, is halfway across the Atlantic.' His tone was mild but the words were sharp and there was an expression in his eyes that came dangerously close to anger. 'Fair play, you want to put your daughter first, that's just right and proper, but don't you dare deny me my feelings and try to put this back in a box to make it easier for you.'

Then he covered his face with his hands and slumped forward. 'Sorry. Sorry. I don't know where that came from. It's not like me to be mildly annoyed, let alone, well, cross about someone's behaviour.'

I took a deep breath. 'No, I'm sorry, Gabriel. It's hard to explain, but when you're a mum you kind of get forced into always going straight for the worst-case scenario. I think we get trained into it; kids don't really get the "if you jump off that roof you might scrape your knee". They aren't impressed by anything less than a broken neck and instant death.' I gave a rueful shrug. 'This is all so new to me. I'm just panicking.'

The familiar smile was back on his face now, creasing around his eyes in a way that highlighted their darkness and the length of his lashes. 'I know. I really do, Katie. I just couldn't bear it if you brushed me off after all this.' He reached out and took my hand. 'This all means something to me. You're the first woman to make me feel that I haven't wasted my life making quilts and learning to crochet rather than strutting bare-chested down the street with power tools strapped to my body.'

The image was so ridiculous that I laughed and any remaining tension between us was gone, carried away on the shafts of sunlight that sneaked their way in through the ill-fitting window. Outside, the sound of chainsaws was gone too, merging into the Doppler effect of a tractor engine chugging its way back up the hill towards the Bridport road, and the insistent trill of the blackbird on the top of the hedge.

'We'd better go and check on Patrick,' I said. 'Poor lad might be floating away down the ford by now.'

'Nope, he's still there. Like a paperweight, keeping the orchard in place.' Gabriel craned his neck around the window corner. 'But you're right. Life must go on. Work to do and all that. I'm trying not to see this as a rare interlude, but if that's what it has to be, then okay. I can cope.'

I gave his shoulder a quick swipe. 'And you can stop doing downtrodden male at me and put some trousers on before I get distracted again. I'm going to make some more coffee.'

The sun was shining in through cracks in the front door, but today, instead of looking worn and semi-derelict, the door looked invitingly Pinterest-worthy. The sun was warming the shiny floorboards rather than illuminating the dust and the kitchen smelled of Gabriel's previous breakfast effort, rather than of damp and woodlice.

Life might not be perfect, but it was looking up.

17

The pub was crowded again as Gabriel and I pushed our way through to where Poppy was waving at us from a corner. No darts match today, but a lot of large-sweatered men in coats and jackets drinking pints and laughing about the storm. Now it was over it was a lot easier to find humour in the fact that cars had floated away, trees had crushed buildings and the high tide had caused the little village of Steepleton to be cut off from the world for several hours.

I was glad I hadn't known about that. And then I felt slightly guilty that I'd been so caught up with Gabriel, and what we'd been doing, that I hadn't found out until it was over. Poppy had been, effectively, marooned that night, after the party. She and Rory had taken shelter with Thea, apparently, who'd impressed Poppy with a bunch of fabric samples and some initial lessons in crochet, and been collected by Karen when the tide dropped.

Poppy told me all about it, at high speed. Rory, sitting beside her, nodded along. I rather suspected that they were holding hands again under the table, but wasn't going to draw attention to it. Karen sat beside Rory looking amused and drinking something that looked retro with a cherry in it on a swizzle stick.

'And everyone thought it was *so-o-o-o cool* the way you galloped into the village and just jumped off your horse and demanded a telephone!' Poppy bent her head over her lemonade. 'They think you're *amazing*, riding through the storm to get help for Granny Mary!'

I sipped an orange juice. Clearly my ride had taken on legendary status already, so I carefully didn't point out that Poppy had thought I'd come to spy on her. My ride was rapidly acquiring a glamour that the rain-soaked miserable slog over the cliffs on an unfit caravan pony had come nowhere near in real life. In a few years' time I expected the story to have mutated so that Patrick became a gleaming ex-racehorse and I would probably have gone in the other direction to become a housewife who'd never sat on a horse before.

But for now, sitting in the warm pub with Poppy safely opposite me and Gabriel carefully not meeting my eye over a glass of tonic water, none of it mattered. We'd got the helicopter for Granny Mary, that was the important thing.

Gabriel stood up. 'Another drink, anyone?' he asked. 'Or we could share a packet of crisps?' He had originally suggested that we eat at the pub, but I'd had to point out that my pecuniary state was such that Poppy and I were pretty much doomed to the contents of the pantry. Meals out were a step too far, with winter heating bills still to be contended with and no job on the horizon.

'Go on, then.' I pushed my glass towards him. There must have been something in my tone, because Poppy looked up sharply, then at Rory, whose eyebrows told me that he and Poppy had had more than one conjectural conversation about my relationship with Gabriel. I gave her what I hoped was a reassuring smile, although there was nothing about Poppy's attitude that was giving off 'worried about being sent away to boarding school so mother can move her boyfriend in' vibes. I'd hope she knew me better than that and tried to silently impart, through the medium of carefully moving closer and nudging her shoulder, that she and I were still the tight unit we'd become since her father had gone.

She pretty much ignored me. Which was, I told myself in a firm, practical way, perfectly normal and to be expected from a fourteen-year-old girl sitting with her boyfriend.

Gabriel's arrival at the bar hadn't gone unnoticed by a group of the jumpered-up men. Three in particular had surrounded him as he leaned across the puddle of spilled beer and ordered.

'It's lanky speccy four-eyed Hunter! Hey, man, you still knitting?' An outbreak of what could only be called 'guffaws' rang into the sudden quiet. Everyone sitting at tables had turned to look, and the atmosphere had taken on a distinct tinge of a Western saloon. I half expected someone to spit a plug of tobacco my way.

Karen met my eye. 'It's like that round here in winter,' she half whispered. 'Cos everyone has known everyone else too long, plus they're all a bit bored. Lookin' for a punch-up and a reason to carry on hatin'.' She shook her head sadly over the dregs of her drink, where the cocktail cherry was bobbing on the surface like an eyeball struggling to see over the rim. 'I despair of these lads. If Rory turns out anything like this, I'm goin' to have to have him put down.'

Rory, who was blamelessly sipping an orange juice, just rolled his eyes.

Gabriel turned around. He was taller by half a head than

his three confronters, and, in comparison to them, it was true that he looked 'lanky'. They all had shoulders that had been honed by hours of humping feed sacks, and spare tyres formed from too many home-cooked dinners and not enough running away from things. Gabriel, with his long hair and cheekbones, looked oddly glamorous, and like a cuckoo chick among naked sparrow nestlings.

'All right, Specs?' One of the men, chunky and with short, tousled mousy hair, put his pint down on the bar as though issuing a challenge. He was wearing a jumper with pictures of reindeer on, which, with the on-end hair and the beer stains, made him look like a giant toddler. One of the other men, whose bobbly sweater strained to cover an unmistakably large belly, made a grab for Gabriel's glasses and the other two gave braying encouragement. The rest of the pub was silent. Staring.

I found I'd curled my hands into fists. Every inch of me wanted to stand up and call them out, but when I moved slightly away from the table Karen shook her head. 'They just wants a reaction,' she hissed. 'Gabe knows to ignore 'em. It'll be okay.'

But Gabriel, to everyone's evident astonishment, pushed himself away from the bar and took a step towards his confronters. 'Yes,' he said mildly. 'I'm still knitting.'

Reindeer-man, also apparently surprised, took half a step back to stop Gabriel causing more bobbling on the front of his jumper. He made a kind of 'Waaay haaay' noise. 'Yer great streak of piss! Knittin' like a woman, and sewin' and all that stuff!' There was a tone to his words that was almost panicked, as though he wasn't used to Gabriel actually replying to him and wasn't 100 per cent sure how he was supposed to react.

Karen had put her hand over her eyes. 'Don't answer 'em back, Gabe,' she muttered. 'It only makes 'em worse.'

But Gabriel had looked across the bar at me. As our eyes met he gave me a tiny, tiny smile, just the merest twitch of a cheek. 'I think he'll be all right,' I whispered back to Karen. She just groaned and lowered her head closer to her glass, but I looked back at Gabriel. He'd straightened his back, stopped doing the cowed kind of stoop that he seemed to adopt around his childhood acquaintances and it brought him a head clear of them, which they hadn't seemed to expect at all. One of the three took a step back. It was the one in a hairy fleece. He'd got 'sidekick' written all over him; the sort of boy who held the smaller ones down so that his friend could hit them. He also had flaming ginger hair, so I didn't imagine his school days had been easy either.

'Can I just point out,' Gabriel said, his voice still mild, but slightly raised, 'that knitting and sewing has bought me a very nice house in Bridport? Whilst you, Andrew, still live at home with your mum, Bren here lives in a van parked next to a silage clamp and Sy is sofa-surfing since Ellie saw sense and kicked him out. I'm making more money from stitching quilts than you lot put together, and I have a wonderful girlfriend, which is, again, not something any of you can boast.'

The silence among the onlookers was profound. From one table came a clink of glass and a whispered, 'Oh, bugger,' but no other sound. It was as if the whole pub were holding its breath.

I waited for the first punch to be thrown and wondered how I'd get Poppy out of the building if a really big fight broke out. Maybe there was a back door? Or we could hide under the table until the worst was over – could Gabriel fight? Maybe I should try and step in to make peace?

But then the bloke with the red jumper straining over his incipient beer belly surprised me by saying, 'He's got a point, y'know, Andy.'

'Andy', who was evidently reindeer-jumper, leaped as though he'd been poked. 'Yer wha'?' he said, wide-eyed and startled.

'Yeah, acshully.' This was ginger-haired bloke, whose hair was clashing so horribly with his friend's red jumper that my vision was flaring. 'He has got a house, like.'

'And I am getting just a *little* bit sick of you still using the same taunts that you've been wheeling out for the last thirty years, you know,' Gabriel went on, calmly. 'Yes, I knit and sew. Yes, I wear glasses and, yes, my parents saw fit to give me a name that can be turned into an insult. Only the knitting bit is down to me and, as previously pointed out, it's got me a decent income and – I hate to say it – but a bit of a fan club in America. Whilst you lot are still pottering about up to your knees in cow shit and have never got further than a big tractor show at the NEC. So come on, guys, grow up.'

He turned back to the bar, where our drinks had now been poured and were awaiting collection. There was a set to his shoulders that told me that he wasn't *quite* sure that nobody was going to swing a punch at him, but that he was trusting to nobody wanting to spill a drink for his safety.

'Well, shit,' said reindeer-sweatered Andy. The other two men were just standing staring at Gabriel as though he'd suddenly ripped his clothes off to display Jean-Claude van Damme under his coat.

Then red-sweater stuck out a hand. 'We've been pissers,' he said. 'Sorry, mate.'

Karen's mouth fell open and the cocktail cherry dropped out.

'Yeah, 's a bit stupid now I comes to think of it too. You're a decent guy, Gay B... I means, Gabriel.' This was hairy-fleece, who, likewise, shook Gabriel's hand.

Andy's reindeer sweater was palpitating. He clearly had a tough choice to make but he wisely went with the masses. 'Okay,' he said. 'I guess it's a truce.'

'No, it's an apology, but I'll take whatever. But no more, okay?' Gabriel shook hands with Andy too. It looked a little more reluctant, but they did it.

And, with my teacher's eyes-in-the-back-of-my-head, I didn't miss Rory mouthing 'Girlfriend. Told you,' to Poppy.

'I thought you was dead there for a minute,' Karen said as Gabriel, looking taller than ever, came over carrying our drinks.

'Tell the truth, so did I.' He sat down next to me. The noise had resumed its previous level; any minute now someone was going to start playing a tinkly old piano in here. 'But I just thought, well, we're too old to behave like we're still in the playground. And there's too many witnesses for them to stamp on my glasses.'

'It was brave,' I said.

'Yeah, well. They're okay guys really, just a bit stuck in their ways. It gets like that in a place like this though – you get cast in a role when you're five and you're just lucky if you break out of it before you get your pension.' He took a sip of his drink and grinned at me. 'And I wanted to break out of my role.'

The group of three was leaving. Red-sweater called, 'Cheers, Gabe!' on his way, and ginger-hair raised a hand in salute. Reindeer-jumper looked a bit dour, but jerked his head in a way that could have meant anything from acknowledging Gabriel to an invitation to come outside and sort it all out with fists and boots, but I deduced that his henchmen were influencing his decision.

'We'll never be best mates, but hopefully they'll stop yelling at me out of car windows now.' Gabriel took another sip. 'And you were right, Katie. The only way to deal with bullies is to call them out on it. I should have done that years ago. Well, around twenty years ago, actually. Then maybe I could have stayed on the swimming team.' A rueful smile and headshake. 'But wisdom is like a kind of acne. It comes when you don't need it and you feel self-conscious and try to cover it up when you do get it.'

'That's practically a T-shirt slogan, right there,' Karen said, chewing the cherry she'd picked up from the table. 'You din't get it off a shirt, did you, Gabe?'

'No, Karen, I did not.' Gabriel sat beside me. 'All my own work. And I have to say, I feel bloody marvellous now.' He dropped his head. 'And I seem to have come over a bit Hugh Grant too, sorry about that.'

'I never knew bullies kept on being bullies when they were grown up,' Poppy said thoughtfully, picking at a raised splinter on the table. 'I thought you grew out of being a shit-head like you grow out of wanting a fringe and sucking your thumb.'

'Poppy!'

'Sorry, Mum. But it is a shitty thing to do, though, isn't it? Bullying, I mean, not wanting a fringe, but, duh, fringes make you look about twelve, everyone knows that.'

'Sometimes people don't just grow out of it, though,' Gabriel pointed out. 'Sometimes they really can't see that they are being, as Poppy so picturesquely put it, "shitheads". Some-times they think they are just joking around and they can't see that the other person can't take what they are saying as a joke because, to them, it isn't.'

'In what world is slowly going blind a joke?' I hadn't liked any of the knitwear musketeers, although I did have a kind of grudging respect for their apologising for their behaviour.

'Ah, they aren't big on empathy.' He gave me a smile that lit those big brown eyes with an expression that reminded me suddenly of Patrick. 'Not really a requisite when you spend most of the day scraping silage off your supermarket jeans.'

'Ooh, bitchy,' Poppy said mildly.

'*That* was alliteration,' Rory said in a tone that implied a continuing conversation and made me feel happier about Poppy's education than any number of glowing school reports.

'And also bitchy.' Gabriel drained his glass. 'Sorry about that. Sometimes I let my inner victim get the last word.'

I heard his phone vibrate in his pocket and he pulled it out and looked at the screen, scanning down to read the full message. The print on the screen was so enlarged that he had to scan for quite a long time. Then he stood up. 'Granny Mary is asking to see me, they think.' Then he sat down again. 'Bugger.'

'I can drive you. Oh.' I looked around the table. 'Only I ought to get Poppy home.'

'Last bus'll be long gone,' Karen observed. 'Plus them schedules is up the creek, what with half the roads still being blocked, so you might not even get there tomorrow. We got up here on the bus and Tim was driving, said he'd never known everything to be in such a state of shambles, and that's sayin' something what with our bus company being two blokes and a terrier.'

'How were we getting home?' Rory asked.

'Walk,' Karen said laconically. 'If you still remember how to.'

'I can drive you home, of course.' I stood up too. 'But Granny Mary sounds quite urgent. Come on, we'll all go to the hospital and I'll drop you at home afterwards.'

Everyone stood up. We were all crowded around the little table, clumped together like skittles in an alley. Rory drained the dregs of his orange juice. 'We should go, then,' he said. 'It might be an emergency.'

'It's Granny Mary.' Karen picked up her cocktail stick. 'I'm going in armed, emergency or not.'

'She's just a sweet old lady,' Poppy said. '*What?* She *is*. She just tells it like it is and being as you've just given us the "stand up to bullies" speech, Mum, then surely you can see that's a good thing.'

I had absolutely no comeback for this piece of teenage logic. Poppy was right, and, in a way, Granny Mary and her plain speaking had, indirectly, got Gabriel and me together. Never mind her being an old lady with nobody else, we *owed* her. 'Right. Let's go.' I palmed my car keys. 'It's going to be a bit of a squeeze in the back, though.'

'They won't mind.' Karen gave her son a look. 'Unless I sit between them, and I'm not going to do that in case I catch Hormones.'

We drove the handful of miles to Bridport along storm-raddled lanes. Drifts of wet leaves were piled in gateways and on corners, bits of tree too small to be called branches but too large to be mere twigs hung from hedges and fallen acorns, still in their caps, scattered the roads like little old ladies in berets. The whole place looked as if a vengeful nature god had done the equivalent of taking his football and going home.

Bridport was mostly deserted when we arrived. The streets were bare and glazed with rain and a power cut was still in evidence from the blacked-out houses. Occasional candlelight flickered from the dark squares of windows but otherwise there was no sign of life.

'It's like a bloody Dickens novel,' Karen observed.

The lights of the hospital were welcoming, and the air of normality and everyday life continuing inside was reassuring. I parked the car whilst Gabriel went inside and then Karen, Poppy, Rory and I milled around in the reception area, searching our pockets for change for the antiquated coffee machine and the table for readable magazines.

Eventually Gabriel found us again. By now Poppy and Rory were sitting side by side on one chair, pretending to be reading a women's magazine but mostly giggling. Karen was flicking the pages of a *Country Life*, sniffing disapprovingly over a politician's choice in soft furnishings. I was leaning against the wall, drinking lukewarm coffee and wondering what the time was.

'Can you come with me, please?' Gabriel's boots squealed to a stop outside and he poked his head into the little waiting room. 'She'd like to see you all. I think. I mean, she's a little bit hard to understand, but, from the look in her eye, if I don't bring you all back with me I think she might kill me with a drip stand.'

We all trooped behind him as he led the way up to a ward where the nurses talked in hushed voices and most of the beds seemed to be occupied by blanket-draped forms who didn't move. This looked serious.

'How is she?' I asked him quietly.

He shrugged and made a face that accentuated the lines of stress that hung around his mouth and eyes like heavy-handed ageing make-up. 'Not good, I don't think,' he whispered back. 'I mean, she's perky enough but – you know Mary. She wouldn't show weakness if her head was hanging off.'

He spun round and we were in the doorway to Mary's room. She lay on the bed, half propped on pillows, looking small and shrunken, although the expression in her eyes was anything but.

'Hello, Granny Mary,' I said. 'Sorry about the crowd. It's been a... complicated sort of day.'

Karen came in behind me while Rory and Poppy hung about in the doorway. They looked a bit shocked and I realised that this was Poppy's first exposure to a properly poorly person. My mother, despite her aches, pains and general incessant complaints, was fit and well and her grand-mère had the air of one who had had herself embalmed at the age of seventy to save time later.

Mary's face still drooped down one side and her right arm and hand lay on the covers, motionless. Her left eye, however, was doing double duty. It fixed me with a burning stare and her left hand beckoned me closer. I had the feeling that she was enjoying herself immensely being the Invalid in the Bed. I hoped she wasn't going to progress to the Madwoman in the Attic.

'How are you, Mary?' With any other older woman I would have stroked her hair. All right, maybe not my mother, who would only have asked if she had a cobweb caught, or Luc's mother, who would have snatched at my wrist and complained I'd upset her *coiffure*. Granny Mary also fell into the 'untouchable' camp. She might have bitten me.

Mary made a noise like Donald Duck. At first I thought she was joking, then realised that it was her attempt at speech, which I, embarrassingly, couldn't understand. To cover my confusion, I smiled in what I hoped was a reassuring way.

'She said you took your time,' Gabriel, who'd had time to get himself accustomed to her speech, translated.

'Sorry. Thought you only wanted Gabe.' Karen came closer to the bed. 'We didn't want to intrude.' Mary gave her such A Look that Karen went a little bit red. 'Yeah, all right, but I never gets to read them posh magazines, 'cept at the dentist, and they've gone right downhill lately. We used to have *The Lady* and *Good Housekeeping* and now it's just that "my boyfriend slept with my mother's teenage lover" stuff, and that's not what you want when your molars are banging on your sinuses.'

Mary gave me a thoughtful look and then pointed at a notepad on her bedside table. I snatched at it with a gratitude born of embarrassment and pushed the pen into her hand. After a moment's fumbling she wrote, in letters that looked as though one of the cottage's woodlice had been dipped in ink and let loose to fight its way through my biscuit collection:

Look after him

Did she mean Gabriel? Or Patrick? Or even Rory, who was hanging on to the door frame, evidently hoping that nobody was going to ask him to do anything. His freckles stood out against a pallor that rivalled Mary's. Poppy was still clutching on to his hand.

'Of course, I will,' I whispered. It didn't really matter who the subject was, I was going to look after them all so hard that I'd creak.

Karen was beckoned to the bed next and a message scribbled, to which she snorted and said, 'Well, that's a given. What did you think I was going to do?' Mary nodded, a curt nod and Karen fell back, to allow Poppy and Rory to sidle into the room.

Poppy surprised me by sitting on the bed. 'It's okay, Granny Mary,' she said softly. 'We're all fine. You don't need to worry about us.' It sounded, very slightly, as though she were giving a form of permission, a reassurance to the old lady that she didn't need to hold on to life out of fear of what would happen when she was gone, and I wondered where my daughter had gained such wisdom because I was pretty sure that it wasn't school.

There was a moment of unspoken communication between them, then Mary patted Poppy's hand and beckoned Rory over, who looked as though fainting might be making his Top Ten List of Things to Do in the Next Five Minutes.

A scribbled note and suddenly the lost colour came back to his face. 'That's... I mean... no! Of course not!'

A few more scribbled words and his freckles took centre stage from the blush again. 'Er, yeah,' he said. 'If I can.'

Another nod, this time a little floppier, and the pen fell from her hand, sprawling onto the notepad, which Rory snatched up. He carefully folded the top sheet over the spiral binding, leaving a clean page and me wondering what it was that Granny Mary had told him. Mary slumped further down on the pillows, her eyes closed, and a slightly scary stillness descended.

'Is she...?' I took half a step forward.

'She's asleep.' Gabriel touched her cheek. 'It must have taken it out of her. But she'll be happy that she's seen you all.'

'What did she tell you?' I asked him as we all shuffled out and back down the corridor. Even Poppy and Rory seemed to have lost a little exuberance in the face of such obvious mortality.

He gave a small smile. Some of those stress lines had faded now, he no longer looked like a pantomime Old Man, although there were dark shadows under those fabulous eyes that gave him a look as though he was seeing into a future he wasn't sure about. 'I'm not going to tell you,' he said.

'Oh. No, of course. Sorry.'

'Why? What did she ask you to do?'

I thought of those words, stark against the whiteness of the page and the room. I still wasn't sure which 'him' they referred to, and, knowing Granny Mary, the uncertainty was part of the message.

'Likewise,' I whispered. 'I've got the feeling it was a "my eyes only" message.'

'Was it about me?' He gave me a worried look, his boots momentarily stuttering a squeaky halt along the lino of the corridor.

'When she's better you can ask her yourself,' I replied pertly, and led the way out to find my car, almost alone in the dark and frost-ridden car park.

18

The next few days passed in the usual blur of activity. Poppy had homework to catch up on and then returned to school for the half term that would lead up to Christmas.

'What do you want for Christmas?' I asked her as we stood out in the paddock watching Patrick, who was glumly rubbing his bottom against a storm-ravaged tree. One of the branches had snapped off and lay, tilted upwards, like a skeleton hand in a murky puddle, above which his hay net swung in the chilly breeze.

'Same as I want for my birthday. A sewing machine, a Versace bag and a pony,' she said, digging her hands deeper into her coat pocket. 'Can we go in now? It's freezing out here and I still have to explain the plot of *Of Mice and Men* and I don't know why cos my teacher should know by now what it's about, otherwise what's the point?'

Patrick stuck out his lower lip and scratched more fervently. The tree rocked slightly and I really hoped it wasn't going to fall any time soon. On one hand, yes, firewood, but on the other, the cost of having to have someone with a chainsaw to cut it up and somewhere to store it to dry. The little shed was full of Patrick's winter feed because I'd weakened and bought some sacks of pony nuts to keep his strength up in payment for the night gallop in that storm. I'd had to get rid of my good chairs in a local car boot sale just to fit the feed in. He was not, as yet, showing much gratitude.

'All right. You go in, I'll just top up his hay and water.'

'Yeah.' Poppy turned, shoulders hunched in the Puffa jacket her father had bought her the day before. At least he'd had it delivered by post rather than turning up in person, although it had caused the postman, who I now knew to be called William, to sniff about the inability of stuffing it through the letterbox.

'You needs a safe place.' He'd sniffed lugubriously, handing me the parcel on the step as I shivered in my dressing gown. 'Then I won't have to get you...' another sniff '... out of bed.'

I have a safe place, I thought now, looking out across the orchard, where Granny Mary's van still sat, looking dark and despondent with no lights on, awaiting her return from hospital. *This*, here, this little damp cottage with the suspect electrics, here I feel safe. I'd even gone so far as to put up a picture of my father. A small one, admittedly, and not in an obvious place, but even so. It was one that had been taken by *Horse & Hound* after the medal presentation and showed Dad, sweaty-headed and grinning, perched on Boomer, just as I always remembered him. Or rather, as I always tried to remember him now. Slowly, slowly the worst memories were being overwritten and I realised that I'd hoarded them. Used them as a barrier. But the more I talked about my father and what had happened – to Gabriel only still, I couldn't quite vocalise it all yet to Poppy – the more distant the memory of that last day became.

As though the thought of Gabriel had summoned him, there he was, at the gate. Tall and dark and, yes, still lanky, but he'd lost something of the Goth that he'd carried and now just looked like a spectacularly attractive man who happened to wear a lot of black.

'Hey.' I squelched a step towards him. 'I thought you said you were staying in Bridport to finish some work?'

He gave me a sad smile and I knew. He didn't have to say the words, and I think he was grateful for that.

'When?' It was all I could force past the lump in my throat.

'This morning.' His voice was rough. 'I've been at the hospital today, sorting stuff out.'

'You should have texted. I'd have come.'

A shrug. 'Nothing you could do.'

We stood for a few moments, separated by the gate, staring silently at Patrick who, with no sense of occasion, lifted his tail and dropped a large pile of dung, then shook himself and dropped his head to the grey wind-scalded grass.

Gabriel had his arms along the top of the gate, one foot on a lower bar. The last of the evening light reflected off his glasses and meant I couldn't see his eyes. 'You didn't have to be alone,' I said quietly.

He smiled. The wind flicked at his hair and he shook his head, like Patrick. 'I know. But I needed to, I think. First time I've ever really felt I had a choice, though, so, yeah.' He shifted his foot, slid a little closer to me and caught casually at my hand. Without taking his eyes from Patrick, he lifted my chilly fingers and gently kissed them. 'It's all better because of you.'

'Apart from the fact that Granny Mary is gone.' I leaned

into his shoulder. Felt the warmth of his lips, the firm bulk of his shoulders under the long black coat and relaxed, just a fraction more.

'Mum!' Poppy's voice drifted out on a beam of sudden light from the kitchen. 'Can you come and tell me what to write about this bl... about this stupid book?'

'I ought to go and tell her about Granny Mary,' I said, not making any move away. 'Are you coming in?'

Another shake of the head and a drift of his hair blew against my cheek. My skin prickled and I suddenly wanted to leap the gate and hurl myself against him, feel the heat of his perfect body and hear him moan against the pressure of my lips. Shock and grief are funny things.

'I'd better get down to Steepleton and break the news to Thea and my parents. Didn't like to do it over the phone.' Gabriel looked across at the open back door, where Poppy was letting our meagre heat escape like a wandering cat across the paddock. 'But some bloke wants to talk to us tomorrow about Granny Mary's last wishes. Is it okay if we come up here to do it?' He gave a rueful sort of smile. 'She probably wants some kind of Viking burial, where we sacrifice Patrick and put them all in the caravan, set it on fire and float it out to sea.'

I shook my head. 'Nowhere near elaborate enough for Mary. She'll want us to repaint the whole van, clean all the tack, clip Patrick out and sell the whole lot in aid of Horses in Distress or something.' Patrick shuffled his cereal-bowl feet over and I felt a brief pang. I'd miss his enormous horsey-smelling presence; the blowing outside the kitchen door when he considered it was breakfast time and the eye staring in at me through the window if I kept him waiting. There was something very reassuring about the sheer substance of him, as though his size and hairy coat kept bad things away.

'She did say, back along, that she was going to donate it all to some charity,' Gabriel said. 'And at least you'll get your garden back.'

And save the money that I was currently spending on feed and hay and the farrier, and I could stop worrying that the van was going to get damaged by falling branches and weather. I looked again at its lonely coldness and really hoped that Mary hadn't left either the van or Patrick to me. There just wasn't the money to keep either of them in the condition they deserved, and having to personally sell either or both would be heartbreaking. At least if her wishes were for me to sell them it would be easier to explain to Poppy.

'Yes. Better that it all goes to a good home.'

Behind me, Patrick farted a huge, impressive trumpet and shook himself; the sound of a mud-crusted mane clonking off nearby undergrowth made me smile ruefully.

'*Mu-u-u-u-um*! Why does Lennie kill the puppy? What is *that* all about?' Poppy's truculent wails came again, and Gabriel pushed himself away from the gate.

'Tomorrow. And I'll bring breakfast.'

'Poppy will be here though – it's an inset day at school.' Another pang. Once inset days would have had me panicking about what to do with Poppy while I had to be at work. I hadn't even had an email back from my contact at the employment agency yet. The vision of the sacks of horse feed gave a guilty throb in the back of my mind.

'It's fine. I wasn't going to ravish you.' And then he gave me another of those smiles, those slightly shy, slightly wicked smiles, that made the blush start somewhere around my ankles and end round the back of my neck. 'Not this time, anyway. Oh, but there is one thing you could do.'

I took a deep breath and really hoped that he wasn't going to ask me to send him any suggestive pictures. I'd have no idea how to go about it, and I was certainly not prepared to go looking for a YouTube tutorial on *that*.

'What?' I knew I sounded slightly cautious.

He gave an odd little half-shrug, almost as though he didn't know how to ask. 'It's... I don't know if you... it's just that there's this picture. In Granny Mary's van. I don't want it to... I mean, someone should keep it.'

'Do you mean the one of her and Rose?'

The look of relief on his face was dramatic. 'She told you?'

'She showed it to me.'

'Wow. She must have really liked you.'

I looked sternly at him. 'Yes. That's the only possible way you could tell. That and the fact I could come out of the van without her teeth marks in my arm.'

We both smiled, slightly sad smiles, at our own personal memories of Granny Mary. 'So, would you...?' he asked, tentatively.

'I'll fetch the picture, yes. I might even put it up on my mantelpiece. You're right. It meant a lot to her. It wouldn't be right to leave it in the van, if it's got to be sold. Unless it's been left to some cousin that has yet to come out of the woodwork.'

'It was her secret,' Gabriel said softly. 'I don't think she'd have wanted any cousins to have it.'

'No. We should keep her secrets for her.'

There was no need for any more words. Gabriel cupped my cheek gently and walked off into the twilight. I ignored Poppy's grumbling half-shout of, 'Mu-u-u-u-u-um!' and went

into the van to retrieve that carefully swaddled bundle from
under the bed.

19

When Gabriel arrived the next morning, a tearful and red-eyed Poppy let him into the front room. I could hear them talking, an occasional interjection from a third voice I didn't recognise, and then furniture moving.

Poppy came to find me in the kitchen. 'Gabe's here,' she said. 'And some bloke who wants to tell us about Granny Mary's... last... wishes.' She choked to a stop, sniffed hard and then said, in a fierce voice, 'It's not *fair!*'

'No, no, it's not,' I said gently. 'But it happens, sadly.'

I remembered my dad's funeral. It had made the six o'clock news. All his fellow equestrian team members had turned up; they'd carried his coffin into the crematorium dressed in their official kit. I'd thought it was weird at the time, so deep in grief that I'd barely registered the day; only later had I realised it had been a mark of respect to see him off in the clothing that had meant so much to all of them. I still had his jacket somewhere, carefully packed away and moved from place to place with me. I hadn't opened the box since I'd put the jacket in. Maybe it retained some of his familiar smell: sweat and horse and aftershave and saddle soap.

'Well, it shouldn't. We'd only just got to know her. I bet this bloke is here to say we have to look after Patrick until someone buys him and the van and that's just mean. It's like... like... Dad wanting the divorce and then still hanging around once he'd told us he was leaving. He should have just *gone*, not moved into the spare room!'

I agreed wholeheartedly with this, but now was not the time to discuss it. 'I know. But we'll find out soon.'

I went into the front room where Gabriel, looking pale and somehow taller in a black leather jacket, was carrying one of the dining chairs across into the window. 'This is Michael Widdowes,' he said, indicating an older man standing with his back to the room. 'And yes, he's apparently heard all the jokes about his name.'

The man turned and advanced to shake hands. 'I'm from Widdowes, Widdowes and Coppergate,' he said. 'Solicitors, based in Dorchester.'

Poppy came in and immediately took up station on the sofa, tucking her legs underneath her. She looked about five. She eyed Michael Widdowes, who had seated himself on the Serial Killer chair, with a slightly defiant air.

Gabriel and I stood behind the sofa and then shuffled closer to one another.

'I can see you, you know,' said Poppy. 'Don't be yukky.'

Gabriel and I shuffled a few feet further apart. I felt his arm creep out behind me and reach for my hand and we entwined our fingers behind our backs. I felt a tiny tingle of rebellion, but kept my face very straight. He, likewise, was looking at Mr Widdowes and not showing any sign of the fact that we were holding hands like teenagers.

Gabriel had a dusting of stubble across his cheeks today, making his cheekbones stand out more than usual, and his eyes looked darker in his pale face. There were small bruises of tiredness under them.

'Are you all right?' I whispered.

'Up getting a quilt finished,' he whispered back. 'Or wrestling alligators, if you prefer to think of me that way.'

I turned to face him properly. 'You know I don't,' I half hissed, hoping Poppy couldn't hear any of this. 'You are perfect as you are, quilts, crochet and all.'

'And you're...'

'You're being yukky.' Poppy didn't even look up from where she was arranging her top to look its best against the sofa's velvet. Mr Widdowes was what she would have called 'so old it's gross', being about fifty, but he was still male and clearly no teenage girl worth the description wanted to look less than her impressive best. 'Stop it.'

'Stopping with the yukky now.' Gabriel gave me a secret grin.

Mr Widdowes cleared his throat. 'I'm here on behalf of the late Mary Louisa Arnold,' he said. 'I'm sure she would rather have been here herself, but circumstances rather overtook her.' He gave a small laugh, and I guessed it was his standard 'putting them at their ease' line, so smiled dutifully. 'She made a will some years ago, but called me to the hospital to amend said will a few days ago. Shall I go ahead?'

He spoke to Gabriel, which I thought was a bit off, seeing as this was my house and everything, but then, Gabriel had known Granny Mary longest and – my mind whispered – maybe she'd left everything to him? But no, Granny Mary knew about Gabriel's eyesight; there was no way she'd have left a pony, even quite a large one, to a man who knew nothing about horses and couldn't see well enough to improvise.

'So, with the exception of a few financial bequests, to... ahem... "Karen, Rory, Mr and Mrs Hunter," and, I am afraid I am quoting here, "that nutcase Thea", the majority of the estate has been left as follows...

'"To Poppy, I leave Patrick, because I know she'll take care of him. I'd like Katie to teach her to ride him properly and how to look after him.

'"To Gabriel, I leave my van. I'll be really happy if he leaves it in the orchard and uses it as somewhere to stop over, now and again or more often, if you know what I mean."'

Mr Widdowes put down the paper that he was reading from and looked at us. 'I do have to say that, despite her condition, Miss Arnold got a bit of a twinkle when she gave me that instruction. I am presuming that you'd know what it's about.'

Gabriel and I looked at one another and tried not to laugh.

'Aw, gross,' said Poppy. 'Will you really teach me to ride, Mum?'

I had a momentary image of my father, lying there in the road with Kelly on top of him and the car halfway through both of them. Remembered that awful, helpless feeling and the sheer shame of not being good enough to ride the young horse past whatever obstacle had spooked him; that knowledge, reinforced by my mother, that my inabilities had caused that whole accident. But then I remembered Patrick's solid body under me, galloping across that clifftop. The way he'd stretched his neck and pushed himself along, unfit and unridden as he was. The way we'd made it through that storm. And Patrick, his sheer good-natured presence in the orchard, his ridiculous black ears and his pirate eye. The image of my father's body faded and was replaced by the image I had of him from his photograph, sweaty, grinning and full of joy.

I could do it. I really could.

'If you want to,' I said. 'We ought to make use of the beast, otherwise he's just the biggest pet in the world.'

'*Mum!*' Poppy rotated on the sofa and leaped up to give me a hug. 'That's *wicked*! Can we get a puppy as well?'

'Don't push your luck.' I hugged her back. Felt a momentary dropping of disappointment in my stomach at the fact that Granny Mary hadn't left Patrick to me. Hadn't left *anything* to me. But then I pulled myself together. Gabriel could come over and stay in the caravan. He didn't need to be around the house with Poppy and me, but he'd be here. We could make this work.

'Well, thank you.' I disentangled myself from Poppy, and my other hand from Gabriel's, and went to shake Michael Widdowes's hand. 'It's wonderful that Granny Mary—'

'Oh, I haven't quite finished,' the solicitor said, looking taken aback at my presumption. 'There is a bequest to you too, Miss Bryant.'

Nobody had called me that for half a lifetime. I returned to my position behind the sofa and Gabriel regained my hand. But down below the back of the sofa, so Poppy couldn't see.

'Mary leaves the residue of her estate, after death duties, expenses and taxes, to you.' He named a figure that was more than I would earn in twenty years of teaching. 'Around about that, we calculate.'

I actually felt my mouth fall open, and then the floor slid sideways. I had to grip firmly onto the velvet back of the sofa to keep myself upright and the pressure of Gabriel's fingers around mine increased for a second. 'She... what? I mean... *what*?'

'God, Mum.' Poppy sounded awestruck. 'You'll be able to get me that Versace bag for Christmas now! I might want the black one, but the blue one is cool too. Maybe I could have both?' she finished, optimistically.

'Oh, yes, Mary Arnold was quite a wealthy woman,' Mr Widdowes, apparently unperturbed by my daughter's acquisitive outburst, carried on. 'She had a fair bit of family money, and she'd invested very wisely over the years.'

'Fuck me,' I said, the world rotating, then remembered myself. 'Sorry, Poppy.'

'But she lived in a caravan!' Poppy chose to ignore my swearing, but I knew it would be brought up next time I corrected *her* for bad language. 'How come she lived in a caravan if she had that much money? Why didn't she just buy a mansion or something?'

'She chose to live in the caravan.' Gabriel sounded as though he'd come to terms with things a lot faster than me. 'She liked the freedom.'

I can get central heating, I thought, my mind reciting the numbers over and over until the zeroes started dancing about behind my eyes. *I can get a new front door. I can afford double glazing... I'll have to okay it all with Keenan first though. And I can get rid of those Serial Killer chairs...*

Gabriel squeezed my fingers again. 'Good old Granny Mary,' he said quietly.

'Yes,' I said. 'Good old Granny Mary.' I swallowed hard.

'Good old Granny Mary,' I repeated, and went to the pantry to break out the secret vodka.

When I got into the kitchen, I looked out through the window into the orchard. Patrick, unconcerned with the life-changing news in the house, was plundering his way along under the big apple tree, nuzzling hopefully at likely looking clumps of grass. The twin triangles of his ears twitched like a pair of argumentative glove puppets, as, over his head on the branch of a tree, the blackbird hopped and paused to chink its tinplate warning. I could almost have sworn that it had a couple of woodlice in its beak.

We're all safe now.

ACKNOWLEDGMENTS

To John Laycock, for his invaluable help with the symptoms and effects of stroke.

MORE FROM JANE LOVERING

We hope you enjoyed reading *The Country Escape*. If you did, please leave a review.

If you'd like to gift a copy, this book is also available as an ebook, digital audio download and audiobook CD.

Sign up to Jane Lovering's mailing list for news, competitions and updates on future books.

https://bit.ly/JaneLoveringNewsletter

A Midwinter Match, another irresistible, feel-good story from Jane Lovering, is available now.

ABOUT THE AUTHOR

Jane Lovering is the bestselling and award-winning romantic comedy writer who won the RNA Novel of the Year Award in 2012 with *Please Don't Stop the Music*. She lives in Yorkshire and has a cat and a bonkers terrier, as well as five children who have now left home.

Visit Jane's website: www.janelovering.co.uk

Follow Jane on social media:

facebook.com/Jane-Lovering-Author-106404969412833

twitter.com/janelovering

bookbub.com/authors/jane-lovering

ABOUT BOLDWOOD BOOKS

Boldwood Books is a fiction publishing company seeking out the best stories from around the world.

Find out more at www.boldwoodbooks.com

Sign up to the Book and Tonic newsletter for news, offers and competitions from Boldwood Books!

http://www.bit.ly/bookandtonic

We'd love to hear from you, follow us on social media:

 facebook.com/BookandTonic

twitter.com/BoldwoodBooks

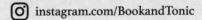 instagram.com/BookandTonic